The eye can be easily fooled

When viewing the products of Gould.

The hand, it is clear,

May be John, Liz or Lear,

Or others whose talents were pooled.

By James Helyar, Curator in Graphics, Spencer Research Library, University of Kansas – with apologies to Mr. Edward Lear, who produced some of Gould's finest illustrations as well as inventing the Limerick.

John Gould – BIRD MAN

by MAUREEN LAMBOURNE
with additional material by
DR. GORDON SAUER and ALLAN McEVEY

Preface by SIR DAVID ATTENBOROUGH

Edited by PATRICIA CONNOR   *Designed by* PAUL CASTELL

Published by Osberton Productions Limited   MCMLXXXVII

RSNC

Patron: HRH The Prince of Wales KG KT GCB

The publication of this book marks the 75th anniversary of the foundation of the Royal Society for Nature Conservation.

With its 47 associated local Nature Conservation Trusts, the Society is active in all aspects of conservation, and is the United Kingdom's largest organisation in this field.

© Osberton Productions Limited
40 Blundells Road, Milton Keynes MK13 7HF
Printed in Hong Kong by South China Printing Co.

John Gould at the age of 45, a lithograph by T. H. Maguire, 1849, from a series of portraits of distinguished scientific men; published by George Ransome. (British Museum)

Note on the authors

Maureen Lambourne *is the great-great granddaughter of John Gould. After taking a degree in Fine Art at Reading University, she worked in the Victoria and Albert Museum and taught Applied Arts in Leicester. She has published articles on John Gould and other animal artists in various journals.*

Allan McEvey *is both a distinguished ornithologist and art historian, areas of scholarship which he has brought together to produce many important works on Gould. Previously Curator of Birds at the National Museum of Victoria in Melbourne, Australia, Mr McEvey has long been the pre-eminent expert on Gould in his country.*

Gordon C. Sauer *has had a forty-year fascination with all aspects of John Gould's life. He has travelled widely in search of material, and published many scholarly works. Based in Kansas, he has had ready access to the unsurpassed collection of Gouldiana in the Ellis Collection at the Spencer Research Library, University of Kansas.*

Publisher's Note

The publishers and author would like to thank the following for their invaluable help in providing material for this book:

Blacker-Wood Library, McGill University
St. Bride's Printing Library, London
The British Museum – Department of Prints and Drawings
The British Museum – Natural History, Zoology Library
The Glasgow Museum & Art Gallery
National Portrait Gallery, London
The Osberton Trust
The Spencer Library, University of Kansas
Victoria and Albert Museum, London
The Zoological Society

Sir David Attenborough
Mrs. Ann Datta
Mrs. Alan Edelsten
Dr. Anthony Edelsten
Brig. David Edelsten
Dr. Geoffrey Edelsten
Mr. Thomas Edelsten
Mr. Rob Fairley
Mr. Michael Foljambe
Mr. James Helyar
Sir Thomas Ingilby
Mrs. Christine Jackson
Mr. Allan McEvey
Dr. Gordon Sauer
Mr. Peyton Skipwith
Miss Judy Tapp
Mrs. Pam Thompson
Dr. Derek G. Twyman

Front cover illustration: Mistle Thrush, Barn Owl and Great Crested Grebe from lithographs by H.C. Richter for 'Birds of Great Britain' and Jacobin Humming-Birds from a lithograph for 'Family of Humming-Birds' II, also by Richter. Back cover illustration: Long-Tailed Tits, a lithograph by W. Hart for 'Birds of Great Britain'. (Osberton Trust)

John Gould, painted in watercolour by his friend Miss Marion Walker in 1875. (British Museum – Natural History)

Contents Page

Preface   7
by Sir David Attenborough

Chapter 1   9
The Acquisitive Naturalist

Chapter 2   19
The Untutored Self-Made Man

Chapter 3   25
A Century of Birds

Chapter 4   34
"Drawing on Stone"

Chapter 5   45
Circumnavigating the Globe

The Father of Australian Ornithology   56
by Allan McEvey

Chapter 6   66
The Finest Points of the Bird . . .

The First Glittering Humming-Bird   89
by Gordon C. Sauer

Chapter 7   95
A Ruling Passion

Bibliography   110

Note: Gould's English and Latin names of birds have been written as they appear in his books. Many of these have variations, or have been altered later, and also differ from present-day scientific descriptions.

Preface *Sir David Attenborough*

If Birds ever had an impresario, it was, surely, John Gould. He was a great talent-spotter. He recognised well the stars with established reputations – the birds of paradise and the humming-birds – and gave them lavish settings in which to show off their splendour. He discovered and launched stars of his own – his monograph on the trogons was the first on that delectable group of birds. He commissioned the most gifted artists to present his beauties to the public in the best possible light – Edward Lear, one of his first, was and remains, to my mind, one of the greatest of all bird illustrators and Joseph Wolf must be close to him. Like all good impresarios, he had firm ideas on what he wanted and he did not hesitate to give instructions to his artists, as his rough pencilled layouts make quite clear. And he had that essential talent for any impresario if he is to remain in business, a shrewd and accurate knowledge of his audience and a knack of presenting his subject so enticingly that the public appetite for it continually grows.

The effect of that last ability of his lingers still.

For my part, I saw plates of his birds of paradise when I was a boy and I remember now the bounce my heart made. How could there be creatures so fantastic, so surreal, so dazzling? Those images were among the stimuli that eventually sent me to New Guinea to watch the living birds. I know now that many of the dramatic postures they adopt in his plates, they never take up in life. That was hardly Gould's fault. Neither he, nor his artists, had seen many of their subjects alive, and all they had to work on, in some instances, were flattened bedraggled skins. But that makes their achievement even more remarkable, for the visions they created are indelible.

Few of us, who remain his devoted public a century after his death, can hope to own one of his massive sumptuous folios complete, but many of us can and do hang plates from them on our walls. It is a delight to welcome this book and exhibition which give an idea of the full range and genius of this remarkable man.

Chapter 1 *The Acquisitive Naturalist*

'Birds, Birds, are all you care about . .' commented John Gould's brother-in-law, writing from Australia in 1840. John Gould (1804-1881), who liked to be known as 'The Bird Man', felt that a lifetime was not enough to learn all that could be discovered about birds throughout the world. Nevertheless his life's work was a remarkable achievement: the production of over forty imperial folio volumes containing some three thousand hand-coloured prints showing birds of every continent, excluding Africa. He illustrated and described the birds of Europe, Great Britain, Australia, Asia, New Guinea, as well as Humming-Birds, Toucans, Trogons, Partridges of America, and the Kangaroos and Mammals of Australia. Two smaller books depict birds collected on the voyages of *H.M.S. Beagle* and *H.M.S. Sulphur*. And Gould's academic work must not be forgot-

Great-crested Grebe (Podiceps cristatus), lithograph by Richter for Gould's 'Birds of Great Britain' V. Gould expressed concern for the bird's future because of the popularity of its feathers for fashion trimmings. (Osberton Trust)

ten – he wrote over three hundred articles and notes for scientific journals.

Although Gould was a man of 'unrivalled industry', as described by a contemporary ornithologist, Prince Charles Lucian Bonaparte, he clearly could not have achieved this phenomenal output single-handed. Gould's success was due not only to his own personal knowledge of birds, but his great ability to organise a group of contributors, artists and craftsmen, as well as his business acumen.

'Everything was overlooked by father' reminisced Gould's daughter. The publication of the Gould books became the work of a production team under Gould's constant supervision. He relied on his long-suffering and painstaking secretary Edwin Prince, who wrote accounts, letters, and made fair copies of the text from Gould's rushed notes for the letterpress printers, Richard and John Taylor, later Taylor and Francis, of Red Lion Court, Fleet Street. His invaluable artists Elizabeth Gould, Edward Lear, and later H.C. Richter, William Hart and Joseph Wolf made drawings or interpreted Gould's rough sketches into fine watercolours. These were copied as outline drawings on stone, and lithographs of the illustrations were then made by the various printers Gould used during his life: C. Hullmandel; Hullmandel and Walton; Walter, Walter and Cohn or Mintern Bros, later to be hand-coloured. The prints were finally assembled with the text into folders for distribution to the subscribers. Incredibly, Gould often had three or even four publications in progress at one time. He wrote for example to a friend, the Reverend Ewing in Tasmania, on 6 September 1849, 'The next parcel will bring you Part 2 *Mammals of Australia* which has just appeared, and which work, now the birds (of Australia) are finished will be regularly proceeded with, *The Birds of Asia* are in abeyance for the present, the *Trochilidae* (Humming-Birds) Part 1 is all but ready, and will I think surpass everything that has yet appeared' . . In modern terms Gould could certainly be called a workaholic!

The era during which Gould worked, spanning the mid-nineteenth century, has been described by Lynn Barber in her book about the popular passion for nature as 'The Heyday of Natural History'. The study of the outdoor world and the pursuit of knowledge about birds, plants, marine life or fossils became a recognised and enjoyable pastime. Gould, in his letter to the Reverend Ewing also expressed the enthusiasm of the period. '. . Your interest in the charming science of natural history is still unabated. May it continue so, for I know nothing that will afford you a greater amount of unalloyed pleasure'. The amateur naturalist the Reverend Gilbert White, in his book *The Natural History of Selborne* (1789), paved the way for the future bird-watcher by his gentle humour, descriptive skill and quiet observation. But although bird-watching became a valid amateur pursuit, it remained a lonely, isolated occupation compared to the convivial pleasures of 'botanising' or finding seashells for collecting tins, with the amusement of getting ones feet 'nicely wet'. Unfortunately, binoculars, the essential aid to bird-watchers today, were not patented until 1859, and the process of bird identification was too often settled by shooting with a gun. Gould himself shot, and collected eggs and nests in a way which now seems callous. He was, however, well aware of the need for bird protection, and in the text of his books often pleaded for the preservation of birds in the wild, such as the golden eagle, osprey, marsh harrier and nightingale. He expressed anxiety for the future of the great crested grebe which in his day was in great demand on account of its beautiful feathers, and killed for use as tippets, muffs or hat trimmings. In the *Mammals of Australia* Gould was prophetic about the fate of the Tasmanian Tiger, (*thylacine* or pouched wolf), which he knew would suffer when settlers cleared the forests – it is now believed extinct, the last authenticated animal having died in Hobart Zoo in 1933.

An irrepressible curiosity about nature led to eccentricity in some nineteenth century natural historians. Charles Waterton (1782-1865) kept the first man-made bird sanctuary at his home at Walton

The Tasmanian Tiger (thylacine), lithograph from 'Mammals of Australia' I (1845-63) after a drawing from life made at London Zoo by H.C. Richter. Regarded as a menace to livestock by settlers, it is now, as Gould predicted, extinct. (Osberton Trust)

Professor Owen in his study, watercolour caricature by Ernest Griset, 1873, of Sir Richard Owen, Superintendant of the Natural History Department of the British Museum, and Mr Bryce-Wight. The cartoon highlights Owen's skills at creating entire reconstructions from fragmentary fossil evidence. The caption reads: 'What a new discovery! Why!! it's a dentigerous Bird!! I'll find a simple name say Odontopteryx Topiapicus. (Victoria and Albert Museum)

Hall, Yorkshire, forbidding any shooting, even of magpies, and in his eighties climbed up tall trees to see the herons' nests. He also described in his *Wanderings in South America* an interest in bats, sleeping with his big toe out of the mosquito net to encourage any thirsty vampire bat to have a drink, and crocodiles, dragging a cayman alligator out of the river to the bank to ride astride its back. Frank Buckland (1826-1880), a pioneering authority on fishes and author of *Curiosities of Nature*, made detailed observations about his menagerie of pets, but also had an extraordinary interest in the edible qualities of ostrich, bison or elephant's trunk.

Sir Richard Owen (1804-1892), an anatomist and palaeontologist who coined the word 'dinosaur' from the Greek word for 'terrible lizards', had an unquenchable enthusiasm for re-creating extinct creatures from the evidence of small pieces of fossil bone, and giving them jaw-breaking names. The *Punch* artist Ernest Griset caricatured Professor Owen in his study, showing a complete 'restored' bird, reconstructed on the slender evidence of the fossil beak. On New Year's Eve, 1853, Owen invited Gould and other eminent men to a dinner inside a reconstructed mould of the Iguanoduon, which had been modelled in cement at Crystal Palace by

Dinner in the Iguanodon model, at the Crystal Palace, Sydenham, an engraving published in the Illustrated London News showing Sir Richard Owen (who supervised the model's construction) and friends, including Gould, dining on New Year's Eve, 1853. (Illustrated London News, 7th January 1854)

Waterhouse Hawkins, one of Gould's illustrators. Gould knew and admired these curious personalities; in comparison his life appears almost conventional, for apart from his considerable pioneer work in Australia, his methods were on the whole that of a 'closet' naturalist, acquiring information, rather than discovering it himself.

The nineteenth century was also an era of natural history collectors. Lionel Walter, Baron Rothschild of Tring, for example, amassed over two million insects. And Miss Margaret Fountaine bequeathed to Norwich Museum 22,000 butterflies. Gould's passion for bird skins was legendary among naturalists in his lifetime. Exotic specimens arrived at his premises, 20 Broad Street, and 26 Charlotte Street, London, from commissioned agents and travellers, friends and relations abroad. In 1846, for instance, Charles Coxen, (Gould's brother-in-law) sent from New South Wales a case containing fourteen parrots, eight bell-birds, one emu, eighteen penguins, one wild cat, four bandicoots, five opossums and two kangaroo rats. Coxen wrote that cassowarys were difficult to get, and was anxious about a Dugong skin in a cask, which was sent but seems not to have arrived! Gould sold 1,847 Australian bird specimens and a collection of eggs to the Academy of Natural Sciences, Philadelphia, for £1,000 in 1847, after the British Museum, then short of money, had refused the opportunity to purchase them. But in 1882, the year after Gould's death, the British Museum Zoological Department, then due to move to the Natural History Museum, South Kensington, paid £3,000 for his collection of 12,395 specimens, which included 5,378 valuable humming-birds.

The best examples of Gould's specimens were stuffed and mounted to be classified, portrayed and described in his books. He used the Linnean system, devised in 1758 by the Swedish scholar Carl Linnaeus (1707-1778) for every living creature, using two names based on Latin/Greek language (binomial nomenclature) describing genera and species. As classical names could be universally understood, this greatly simplified the chaos of terminology that had existed before. Care had to be taken that priority was given to the earliest person who had allocated the specimen with an adequate description in print; sometimes confusion occurred when it was found that a specimen thought to be new had in fact been given an earlier name. New species were sometimes given complimentary names, such as the British Bewick's swan *(Cygnus bewickii)* named in honour of the wood-engraver of birds, Thomas Bewick; or the

Bewick's Swan (Cygnus minor), *lithograph by Richter from a drawing by Wolf for 'Birds of Great Britain' V. (Osberton Trust)*

The Empress Brilliant (Eugenia imperatrix), *lithograph by H.C. Richter from 'A monograph of the family of humming-birds' IV (1849-61). Gould dedicated this beautiful bird to Eugénie, Empress of France. (Osberton Trust)*

humming-bird, Empress Brilliant *(Eugenia imperatrix)* dedicated by Gould to the beautiful, Eugénie, Empress of France. Prince Albert was designated a lyrebird *(Menura alberti)* by Gould in 1850, Queen Victoria a riflebird *(Ptiloris victoriae)* in 1849, and the young Princess of Wales, a parakeet *(Polytelis alexandrae)* in 1863. The die-hard, Charles Waterton, disagreed with these fanciful complimentary names, which he thought were designed to secure patronage; he believed that the English descriptive words of wood-owl or carrion-crow were good enough. He created a hoax creature, a taxidermic freak made up from the skin of a Red Howler monkey with a face distorted to resemble human features, which he called a 'Nondescript' to fool the naturalists who were so keen on finding new species.

Nevertheless, the Linnean system survived and the Linnean Society, founded in 1788, attracted the leading naturalists of the time. Gould became an Associate of Linnean Society at the early age of twenty-six, and in 1843 he was elected Fellow of the Royal Society. Gould's nomenclature is still used for many species, especially in Australia; but the most notable bird bearing the Gould name is the magnificent little Gouldian finch *(Amadina gouldiae)*, now *Chloebia gouldiae*, dedicated to Elizabeth Gould,

The Gouldian Finch (Amadina gouldiae), a drawing in water-colour attributed to H.C. Richter for 'Birds of Australia' III. Discovered by Gould's explorer, John Gilbert, it was dedicated to Elizabeth Gould in memory of her work in Australia. (Blacker-Wood Library, McGill University, Canada)

Amadina gouldiae , *the finished lithograph from Richter's drawing. (Osberton Trust)*

which Gould described as having all the colours of the rainbow. This radiant little gem was found by John Gilbert, the explorer, on an island in Van Dieman's Gulf, Northern Australia in 1840-41; its green, purple, yellow and red plumage is a favourite among bird fanciers. Gould's name is also remembered among animals; there is even a Gould's wattled bat, (*Scotophilus Gouldi*).

The Budgerigar, or Warbling Grass Parakeet (Melopsittacus undulatus), *lithograph by Elizabeth Gould for 'Birds of Australia' V. Gould introduced the first pair of live 'budgies' into England from Australia in 1840. (Osberton Trust)*

Perhaps Gould's most extraordinary achievement was the introduction of the budgerigar to England. In Australia, during 1840, he watched these fascinating little grass parakeets *(Melopsittacus undulatus)* which flew in flocks 'up to a hundred strong'. He took two live 'budgies' (the aboriginal name of Betcherrygah became corrupted to Budgerigar), reared by Charles Coxen back to England – 'the most animated, cheerful little creatures you can possibly imagine'. Their 'sprightliness of manner' made them great favourites and excellent cage birds. They are now popular pets throughout the world.

Gould was an able salesman. While the books were in preparation he organised a list of subscribers, and, in order to guarantee payment, he stated that 'The Author makes it a *sine qua non* that the name of every subscriber shall be given, and the subscription paid on delivery, or at least annually; and he trusts that no person will commence the Subscription without continuing it to its close.' In 1866 there were said to be one thousand subscribers, including 12 Monarchs, 11 Royal Highnesses, 16 Dukes, 6 Marquises, 30 Earls, 5 Counts, 31 Honourables, 61 Baronets and one Bishop! The books were also bought by 107 libraries, clubs and institutions. His prices, for example the seven volumes (600 plates) of the *Birds of Australia* cost £115, ensured that only the well-off could afford them. Today this sum is the amount one might pay for a single illustration from a London printseller's shop.

Lyme Regis, Dorset, 1814, where Gould was born, engraved by W.B. Cooke from J.M.W. Turner's drawing for the 'Southern Coast' series. The view shows the breezy coastline of the fishing town and resort with its breakwater, the Cobb, in the distance. (Victoria and Albert Museum)

Chapter 2 *The Untutored Self-Made Man*

John Gould was born on September 14th 1804, at Lyme Regis on the Dorset coast. This small fishing town was fast becoming a fashionable resort, immortalised by Jane Austen (who stayed there that very autumn) in her novel *Persuasion*. She described the fresh-feeling sea breeze and the bracing promenade along the Cobb, the old stone pier leading to the sea. A few years later, a poor girl call Mary Anning was selling sea-side 'curiosities', mainly ammonites, at Lyme to tourists. She became famous for her valuable fossil collection; amongst her geological discoveries were pieces of a *plesiosaur* in 1824, and, in 1828, a *pterosaur*, the first flying reptile ever found in Britain.

This new awareness of nature had a far reaching influence on both writers and scientists. In the *Birds of Great Britain*, written in late middle age, Gould describes with Wordsworthian passion his first thrill of discovering nature, when his father, a gardener, held him up as an infant to see the vivid blue eggs in a sparrow's nest. 'From that moment', he wrote, 'I became enamoured with nature and her charming attitudes; it was then I received an impulse which has not only never lost its influence, but has gone on acquiring new force through a long life'.

When Gould was still very young, his family moved to Stoke Hill, near Guildford, Surrey, and he later recalled happy memories of the wild commons and heaths of the Surrey countryside. Here, no doubt, he took part in the typical games of egg-collecting and bird-nesting played by country children, so well described by Flora Thompson in *Lark Rise to Candleford* from memories of her Victorian childhood. 'Boys saw no cruelty in demolishing nests, and taking every egg they found,' she relates. 'To them, the idea that anything so small as a mother chaffinch could feel was ridiculous. They were thinking of the lovely long string of threaded eggshells, blue and speckled and pearly white, they hoped to collect and hang up at home as an ornament'. Gould described how he and his friends collected 'particoloured strings of eggs' which they 'delighted to festoon on walls' but which were rigorously destroyed by their games before the end of the year. He recalled the custom of the cottagers, to hang a dried kingfisher from the ceiling, its movements supposed to point the direction of the wind, 'a superstition', he wrote, 'now, like many others, happily abandoned'. And he commented on the wilful ignorance of some country folk, who, despite the richness of bird life around them, thought only of birds as food or vermin, and knew little of their names or habits.

It is not known where Gould went to school, or the extent of his education. He did not attend a university or art college, and regarded himself as a self-made man, his ornithological knowledge gained from his own observation and experience. The text in his books shows a fine feeling for language, and he developed a fluent style, though perhaps too verbose and ponderous for our tastes today. A lack of academic education did not deter him from using classical allusions and poetic quotations. One of the longest was about the humming-bird named *Cometes Phaon*, misnamed in Gould's opinion, because the classical love story of Phaon and Sappho could not

Phaon Comet (Cometes Phaon), a lithograph by H.C. Richter for 'Family of Humming-birds' III. Gould used the classical story of Phaon and Sappho in describing these birds. (Osberton Trust)

20

apply to these belligerent birds, 'their general conduct appearing to be actuated by the Furies, rather than the Loves, engaged as they are in continuous strife with one another'. Manuscript notes for the *Birds of Great Britain* reveal that Gould liked friends to supply him with relevant verses and quotes from literature; for example Miss Marion Walker, an artist and family friend, noted down suitable passages from Shakespeare and the Bible which related to birds.

'A naturalist may be anything, everything', quotes Lynn Barber from G.H. Lewes's *Sea-side Studies*. In the early nineteenth century, natural history embraced many sciences such as botany, zoology or geology, which could not be studied at university level, as no scientific courses other than medical were then available. Gould was single-minded in his interest in birds and animals – a colleague said that he hardly ever read a book, but was very fond of bird-skins! The theoretical philosophical and religious disagreements of the age were disregarded and avoided by Gould in his writings. In spite of the violent Darwinian controversy which raged in the 1860's, no comment was made, even in letters, either to support or oppose the new theories.

In 1818, the family moved to Windsor, where Gould's father was appointed a gardener in the Royal Gardens. At the age of fourteen, John Gould started to learn the same trade and was placed under the care of John Townsend Aiton, son of the famous William Aiton (author of *Hortus Kewensis*), head gardener at Kew and other royal gardens. One of his tasks, as related in Lowell Reeves' book *Men of Eminence* (1863), was to pick 'many a bunch of dandelions for Queen Charlotte's German salad'. This story is a curious one, as Queen Charlotte died that same year, in November 1818, and her final visit to Windsor was from 10th to 14th April to see poor, mad, King George III, who lived a lonely, ghostly existence in the North Terrace until his death in 1820. His son, George IV, later transformed the straggling, comfortless building into a flamboyant palace, with the round towers and crenellated walls we can see today. In Windsor Great Park Gould would have seen fine herds of deer, and he was perhaps allowed to visit the unusual animals housed at the royal menagerie near Sandpit Gate.

In his spare time, Gould became proficient at egg-blowing and taxidermy, for when he was only fourteen years he was already able to prepare specimens with great skill. At Eton College nearby, there was a 'Boys Museum'; Gould traded blown eggs and stuffed birds to the Eton scholars – an early start to his career as taxidermist, ornithologist and salesman.

Gould continued his work as a gardener at Ripley Castle, Yorkshire, where he is thought to have trained in the art of forcing plants under glass. Records of the pay entries at Ripley Castle, which have kindly been researched and contributed by the present Sir Thomas Ingilby, show that Gould was employed between September 18th 1823 and February 26th 1825, at twelve or thirteen shillings for the week, depending on whether he worked six or seven days. Ripley Castle had been the seat of the Ingilby family since 1350, but Sir William Ingilby (1784-1854), who then owned the estate, had elaborate plans to remodel the grounds on a grand scale. When Gould was there an extensive range of greenhouses in the castle gardens (twice their present length) had just been built, some picturesque houses based on a village in Alsace Lorraine were in the process of construction, and a pleasure garden, woodland walks and gazebo were planned. Why Gould left after a year and half is not known, but some alteration in the gardening staff seems to have occurred at this period, as two other men left the following week. So, at the age of twenty, Gould moved back to London, where he abandoned his gardener's career, and set up in business as a taxidermist.

Taxidermy, the art of preparing and mounting skins in a lifelike manner, had become a much prized craft in the nineteenth century. New skins were continually arriving from abroad for classification, and owners wished to preserve the exotic creatures which had died in their parks and menageries. Attempts had been made since the seventeenth century to preserve specimens, but almost nothing has survived. One exception is the stuffed African grey parrot (*Psittacus erithacus*) displayed beside the wax effigy of one of Charles II's mistresses, the Duchess of Richmond who died in 1702, in the crypt of Westminster Abbey. Most specimens from voyages abroad were stored in spirits, but habitually disintegrated or were attacked by insects; only one of Captain Cook's birds survives. The spices, tobacco and other aromatic substances which were used to 'preserve' specimens merely caused decay. The more effective arsenic soaps, replacing dangerous arsenic liquid mixtures as 'preservatives', were introduced to England from the Continent in the 1820's. William Swainson in 1840 described a mixture of camphor, arsenic, soap, salt of tartar and chalk, which could be made into soap paste or cakes. He emphasised that great care had to be taken that the fingers and nails were well washed afterwards, otherwise sore fingers would result! Skilful taxidermists, in the nineteenth century, tried to make sure that as much flesh and tissue as possible were removed, before the specimen was dried and mounted with tow and wires. Charles Waterton had his own method of soaking skins in 'corrosive sublimate dissolved in alcohol', which 'penetrated every pore', and kept the skin moist and flexible, so that it could be 'moulded at will'; in this way he mounted specimens without the use of elaborate wires and supports. It is not known who instructed Gould, but animal preservers, who were sometimes also shoemakers, were growing in numbers, and the popularity of displaying stuffed birds and animals under glass or 'shades' increased as the century advanced.

Soon after Gould's return to London an event took place which was to be of fundamental importance to his career. This was the formation on April 29th 1826 of the Zoological Society of London, an offshoot from the Linnean Society, to 'promote zoological knowledge'. Its aims were to 'form a collection of living animals, a museum of preserved animals, with a collection of comparative anatomy, and a library concerned with the subject'. A house, 33 Bruton Street, was taken for offices and a museum, and a site at Regent's Park for live exhibits. In 1827,

John Gould, after a competitive exhibition of the skill of various applicants, was appointed 'Curator and Preserver to the Museum'. He had already received a commission from the King, George IV, for his taxidermy; a receipt, dated 1825, survives in the Windsor Castle Royal Archives from John Gould, 'For preserving a Thick knee'd Bustard £1.5.0.'. In the following years he 'preserved' an emu, horse, deer, monkey and many other animals and birds at varying prices. A billing for work in 1826 came to £41.12s.5½d., which included preserving 'two Mouse Deer, two Cotamundy's' and an ostrich, and in 1828 the price for stuffing another ostrich was £7.0.0. and a King Vulture was £1.10s.

The largest and most exciting commission Gould received was to stuff George IV's historic giraffe. This poor animal, a present from Mehemet Ali of Egypt, had travelled across the desert at times strapped to the back of a camel. Its brother, which was considerably larger, was given to Charles X of France, and after a walk of over a month from Marseilles to Paris in a historic procession, lived in Paris's Jardin des Plantes for another eighteen years. In contrast, George IV's giraffe was never strong and died about two years after its arrival, languishing sadly in Windsor Great Park. The King's attachment to the

STATE of the GIRAFFE

Little hope is now entertained of the recovery of the Giraffe since the last attack he is unable to rise without the assistance of slings - every attention is paid him but his friends without fail J. having passed...

'The State of the Giraffe', 1829, a caricature print by William Heath showing George IV and Lady Conyngham trying to lift the animal by pulley. The first live giraffe in England, presented to the king by Egypt, is depicted as an ailing pet. It lived for nearly two years in Windsor Great park before being stuffed by Gould. The caption predicts its fate: 'I suppose we shall have to pay for stuffing him next'. (Lambourne Collection)

giraffe was seized on by his caricaturists as an example of his extravagant and bizarre taste. One caricature *The Camelopard or a New Hobby* shows the obese George IV and his bulky mistress Lady Conyngham riding on the giraffe. Another by William Heath, called *The State of the Giraffe*, portrays the enfeebled animal being raised by a pulley. A small note in the margin adds the remark 'I suppose we shall have to pay for stuffing him next'! *The Windsor and Eton Express* stated on October 17th 1829, 'Messrs Gould and Tompkins of the Zoological Gardens are now dissecting the Giraffe which expired on Sunday last. We understand when the skin is stuffed, His Majesty intends making it a present to the Zoological Society'. A bill in Windsor Castle Royal Archives for 1830 shows that Gould received £148.10s. for stuffing a giraffe, a crane and two lemurs. The skin and skeleton were given by George's successor William IV to the Zoo's collection, where it could be seen 'beautifully prepared' until about 1855, when the collection was disbanded. The giraffe was purchased by a Dr. Crisp, but its whereabouts today are unknown.

Chapter 3 *A Century of Birds*

In his position as 'Curator and Preserver' to the Zoological Society, Gould had many opportunities for zoological research, and to meet leading naturalists of the day. 'Gould is a man of great industry – he has the advantage of the Zoological Society's Museums Gardens etc. and is in correspondence with Temmick, Selby, Jardine and the rest of Scientific gentry', wrote the envious John James Audubon. He had arrived from America in 1826 and was seeking to find subscribers for his own magnificent books.

The Zoological Museum began with 146 specimens, including a clouded tiger donated by Sir Stamford Raffles, and animals from Captain (later Sir John) Franklin's first Arctic expedition. Some live animals had temporary accommodation while the Gardens were in preparation; especially memorable was a wanderloo monkey, described as a 'right merry fellow', who was adept at snatching hats and, it was rumoured, once grabbed a well-powdered wig from a bishop who ventured too near. Visitors were admitted to the Museum at 33, Bruton Street and the Gardens in Regent's Park from 1828 'on the written order of a Member, and payment of a shilling' – the order allowed the holder to introduce, each for the same sum, as many friends as he liked. There was also a temporary aviary at Bruton Street, and it was probably there that Gould met two people of importance for his future career: Elizabeth Coxen, later his wife, and the young Edward Lear.

Elizabeth Coxen, born in July 1804, and two months older than John Gould, came from Ramsgate in Kent, her family having naval and military connections. At the time she met Gould, she was the only remaining child still in England of a family of nine – her two surviving brothers, Stephen and Charles Coxen, had emigrated to Australia. She was placed as a governess to teach French, Latin and

Music and perhaps Art, to the nine-year-old daughter of a family near Buckingham Palace. In a homesick letter to her mother she describes her pupil as a 'perfect child in mind and manners', which increased her isolation as there were no feelings she could share, and often she felt 'miserably, wretchedly dull'. She continued 'The wind is howling a good deal tonight and I think of my darling brother much and of the beloved lost one. I feel I shall get very melancholy here'. Her bedroom overlooked the Palace and Barracks and she wrote 'were it not that I see constantly living things really moving backwards and forwards there I should fancy I was to be shut up here for ever without knowing anyone who could enter one's feelings'. Fortunately, Elizabeth Gould's life took a different turn from the endless spinsterhood of many poor governesses, for although she felt that she would not meet 'society', a visit, perhaps a sketching trip with her charge, to the Zoological Society, and her meeting with the new young curator, resulted in their marriage at St. James Piccadilly on January 5th 1829.

Elizabeth Gould's quiet but sympathetic manner, her sensitivity and her cultured background must have been in sharp contrast to her husband's assertive and bustling ways. Those who knew them

Elizabeth Gould, née Coxen (1804-41). This oil portrait, by an unknown artist, was painted after her death aged only 37. She is holding an Australian cockatiel (Nymphicus hollandicus) a family pet brought from Australia. (Private collection)

remarked on their different temperaments. Lady Franklin in Tasmania, for example, when she first met the Goulds, thought they seemed 'nice sort of people'; but whereas Mrs. Gould appeared 'a very unassuming and diffident person', Mr. Gould was described as 'fully conscious of his importance as a lion'. She added, charitably, that she felt Mr. Gould was justified in his assertiveness, for she did not see why 'a bird fancier should come all the way to the Antipodes in pursuit of his particular fame, and not think better of himself for it'. John James Audubon described Gould as 'rich and renowned' and Mrs. Gould as 'plain, fine woman' and a 'skilful lithographer of his birds'. As partners the Goulds complemented each other, and their talents resulted in the success of the first Gould enterprise, the volume of *A Century of Birds hitherto unfigured from the Himalaya Mountains*. Shortly after their marriage Gould had acquired a collection of varied bird skins, many new to British naturalists, from the hill countries of the Himalayas. When Gould had stuffed and mounted them, he saw their artistic qualities and visualised how well they would look in an illustrated book. Eighty plates depicting a hundred birds were issued in folders between 1830 and 1833.

The Goulds' new venture began just when several fine bird books were in production. 'Works on Birds of the World are innumerable' wrote Audubon in disgust in 1836. But pride of place must go to his own magnificent *Birds of America* (1827-1838), now the most expensive bird books in the world. At a recent auction one set (four volumes, 435 prints) sold for a million pounds. However, at the time John Gould's career was secure and prosperous compared to that of John James Audubon (1785-1851). Born in Haiti, of Creole and French parents, and brought up in France, he emigrated when eighteen to Pennsylvania and after several business failures and bankruptcy, travelled along the Ohio and Mississippi rivers and through the southern states of North America. He made hundreds of drawings of birds set in their natural habitat which have an animation unknown in any other bird illustrator's work. Unable to find a publisher in America, he arrived in Liverpool in 1826 where he exhibited his pictures and caused a stir by his wild and romantic appearance. Nicknamed 'The American Woodsman', because of his fringed buckskin jacket and chestnut ringlets, he was wined and dined by society. His illustrations were eventually made into magnificent aquatints at Edinburgh by William Lizars in 1827. But a strike by colourists forced him to find another collaborator, the London engraver Robert Havell. Audubon insisted that the aquatint plates should represent the birds life-size, using double-elephant folios at immense cost. This meant that he was constantly worried by flagging subscriptions during the work's production, which took nearly twelve years.

Gould's method of using mounted specimens as models for his plates was very different from Audubon's, who pinned and positioned newly killed specimens on a board in life-like poses, and painted them quickly before their colours faded or looked dead. Audubon thought most bird pictures of the time were dull and lifeless, but gave the Goulds some mild praise, 'although these works are not quite up to Nature, both (the Goulds) deserve great credit'. A comparison of their different styles, the one dramatic, the other pragmatic, can be seen in some of the birds they both illustrated, such as the lesser tern and mallard ducks. Audubon's tern zoom across the sky, whereas Gould shows a family group with chicks nestling on the shingles; the American mallard noisily waddles, shuffles and stretches in contrast to the English pair paddling serenely side by side.

Lesser Tern (Sterna minuta), *an aquatint from 'Birds of America' (1827-38) by J.J. Audubon.*
(Victoria and Albert Museum)

28

Mallard (Anas platyrhynchos), *an aquatint by J.J. Audubon from 'Birds of America' (1827-38). Audubon drew these 'untamed duck of the swamps' in Louisiana or Mississippi between 1821 and 1825. (Victoria and Albert Museum)*

Little Tern (Sternula minuta), *a lithograph by H.C. Richter (1865) for Gould's 'Birds of Great Britain' V (1862-73), Gould watched these birds nesting on the shingle at Dungeness in June 1864. (Osberton Trust)*

Mallard (Anas boschas), *a lithograph by Joseph Wolf and H.C. Richter for 'Birds of Great Britain' V. (Osberton Trust)*

Both ornithologists greatly admired the small wood-engravings of Thomas Bewick in his classic *A History of British Birds* (1797-1804). Each page is illustrated with a small portrait of a bird and a lively vignette of a farmyard or village scene as the tailpiece, based on observations of rural life in the Northumbrian countryside. Audubon travelled to Newcastle-upon-Tyne to see Bewick, aged seventy-five in 1827, and found him 'a perfect old Englishman' and a 'son of Nature to which he owed nearly all that charac-

Rook (Corvus frugilegus), a wood-engraving by Thomas Bewick (1758-1828) for his 'A History of British Birds' (1797-1804). Both Audubon and Gould admired Bewick's vignettes of everyday birds placed in carefully observed scenes of the Northumbrian countryside.

terised him as an artist and a man'. Gould praised Bewick in his introduction to the *Birds of Great Britain*, and Bewick's Birds were in the catalogue of his library after his death. Gould's own plates of everyday birds such as the robin, sparrow or owl are similar in conception, though very different in technique to Bewick's delicate engravings on small pieces of box wood.

On the same large scale as Audubon's books were the less flamboyant engravings of Prideaux John Selby's *Illustrations of British Ornithology* (1821-1834). But they were rather overshadowed by Audubon's work, and later, from 1834 to 1843, Selby collaborated with Sir William Jardine in publishing the more popular, inexpensive pocket-sized *Naturalist's Library* of small hand-coloured engravings by various artists. Most nineteenth century illustrators were at pains to convey realism and avoid the toy-like stiffness which characterised the hand-coloured engravings of the eighteenth-century naturalists such as George Edwards (1694-1773) and his contemporaries.

Gould's contemporary William Swainson (1789-1855), although little remembered, was an important innovator of bird illustration as he used the newly invented printing method of lithography, rather than the stiffer line of engraving for his work. A traveller in Brazil, taxidermist and writer, he had a chequered career which involved a published squabble with Audubon over the terms for collaborating with Audubon's *Ornithological Biography*, and arguments with others about his own strange methods of bird classification, which may have caused his decision to emigrate to New Zealand in 1840. His *Zoological Illustrations* (1820-1823) and *Birds of Brazil and Mexico* (1834-1836) were small books with beautifully hand-coloured and accurately depicted perched birds with little background. Illustrations of birds from Sir John Franklin's first land expeditions in northern Canada, published in 1831, were described as 'greasy daubs of Lithography' by a contemporary critic who preferred fine engraving, but these experiments paved the way for the grander luxury productions of imperial folio format, (approximately 22 inches x 16 inches), introduced by the young Edward Lear and later produced by John Gould.

Edward Lear (1812-1888) is now best remembered for his limericks and comic verse – author of

Edward Lear, drawn in Rome at the age of 28 by a Danish artist friend, Wilhelm Marstrand, three years after leaving Gould's employ to live in Italy. (National Portrait Gallery)

The Quangle Wangle's Hat and *The Dong with the Luminous Nose*. These inventive fictions were written as a relaxation from his zoological drawing and landscapes, and it was quite by accident that his strange verses with funny pictures became more popular than his serious work. Lear had an unhappy childhood; the 20th of 21 children (many of whom died in infancy), he was neglected by his mother and looked after mainly by his older sisters. Family financial losses caused him to start earning money at fifteen by the hack work of colouring screens and fans, or making medical drawings of diseases for prices varying from nine pence to four shillings each.

His introduction to ornithological work came through Prideaux Selby, (he drew a Great Auk for Selby's *Illustrations of British Ornithology*) and he began painting parrots at the newly opened Zoological Society when he was eighteen. His book of parrots, *Illustrations of the Family of Psittacidae* (1830-1832), of 42 plates issued in parts, was a remarkable undertaking as it was the first ever book of a family of

birds. He planned to portray all the species then known, and the majority of illustrations are from living birds. His drawings show superb draughtsmanship, embellished with rich washes and colour notes. The finished prints are often of breath-taking reality, and the soft lithographic chalk conveyed realistically the feeling of the soft down or ruffled feathers of the macaws and cockatoos. Unfortunately, the venture was not a financial success. Lear found difficulty in persuading his 175 subscribers to pay enough for him to cover the cost of the colourists and printers. His rooms were overflowing with parrot prints, and he wrote to a friend that there was no room for visitors except to sit in the grate! Although the illustrations were praised, (Swainson judged the red and yellow macaw as equal to Audubon's work), Lear did not complete the full number of prints as he had intended, but stopped after the 42nd plate, and produced no text. John Gould bought the remaining stock and completed some of the orders but plans for finishing the last two parts were never fulfilled.

Blue and yellow macaw (Macrocercus ararauna), *a lithograph by Edward Lear for his 'Illustrations of the Family of Psittacidae, or Parrots' (1830-2). Lear was only 18 when he drew the parrots from life at the Zoological Society in London, and began the publication, 'the first book of the kind drawn on stone in England of so large a size'. (Victoria and Albert Museum)*

Chapter 4 *"Drawing on Stone"*

Dr. Richard Bowdler Sharpe, who completed Gould's publications after his death, describes in a short biographical memoir how Gould inaugurated his publishing career by talking of his plans with his wife, Elizabeth. 'But who will do the plates on stone?' she asked. 'Who?' replied her husband. 'Why, you, of course'.

Gould had decided to print his illustrations by the recently discovered process of lithography, used with such artistic success by Edward Lear. The method had been invented in 1798 by Alois Senefelder (1771-1834), a German working in Prague who was looking for a cheap method of printing his own plays. He visited London in 1800, and guarded his secret until he obtained a patent for the process, which he called 'polyautography', of printing from stone. It was granted by George III in 1801, but as is often the case, the unbusinesslike Senefelder did not himself benefit from his invention. He sold his

patent and left England for Germany. It was not until 1819, when the printer and book-seller Rudolph Ackermann demonstrated the process to the Society of Arts with a press sent from Munich by Senefelder himself, that there was a revival of interest in England. He published two manuals, a translation of Senefelder's *A Complete Course of Lithography* (1819), and in 1824, Hullmandel's *The Art of Drawing on Stone.*

Charles Joseph Hullmandel (1789-1850), an Englishman of French descent, was a landscape painter who had met Senefelder in Munich on his way back from a sketching trip. The title page of Hullmandel's book shows an elegant young lady, with a desk and footstool, seated with crayon poised ready to 'draw on stone'. Her relaxed pose and fashionable dress suggests that this quick and unmessy process was a suitable pastime for an aspiring lady artist like Mrs. Gould. The great advantage of draw-

*Male and female Shrikes (*Coccothraustes icterioides*) drawn in ink and watercolour by Elizabeth Gould for 'A Century of Birds from the Himalaya Mountains' (1830-33). John Gould stuffed and set these rare birds on perches for his wife's first illustrations. (Spencer Library, University of Kansas)*

ing on stone was that no apprenticeship was needed as was the case for engraving metal or cutting into wood. Hullmandel's book showed how the lithographic chalk could be placed in a holder called a 'portcrayon', or, if this was too heavy, a light container made from a swan quill fixed to a piece of cedar or a grooved piece of cork. This was used like a pencil, and when held at a slanted or almost vertical angle could make light or dark lines. The chalk could be sharpened for delicate work and richness in drawing could be achieved by gentle shading. Although Hullmandel was chiefly interested in the artistic effects of landscape and topography, especially tonal effects, the diagrams in his book also show chalk drawing methods appropriate for zoological work. Amongst examples of lithographic technique which Hullmandel collected in a scrapbook of experiments (c. 1820-1840), now in St. Bride's Printing Library, London, is a print by W.H. Kearny of an Alpaca, showing a llama with a superbly woolly coat. Chalk lithography became especially adaptable for portraying the soft fur of such animals or the downy plumage of birds. Hullmandel's instructions in *The Art of Drawing on Stone* were written for potential artists and draughtsmen; printing techniques were not described as he hoped clients would have their work printed at his press in Great Marlborough Street, London.

The process of lithography is simply surface drawing with special greasy crayons on a prepared finely-grained flat slab of limestone. To obtain a print the stone is further washed with weak nitric acid, wiped with gum arabic, and then dampened. When oily ink is rolled on, it adheres to the greasy crayon and not to the moistened stone, on the principle of antipathy of grease to water. After paper has been laid on the inked stone, and passed through a special press, a print is made showing the image of the drawing in reverse.

Elizabeth Gould quickly learnt to 'draw on stone'. By December 1830 Gould was able to forward the first number (four plates) of his new work, *A Century of Birds hitherto unfigured from the Himalaya Mountains* (1830-1833) to the naturalist Sir William Jardine: 'It is Mrs. Gould's very first attempt at stone drawing which I hope you will take into consideration'. By the next month Prideaux John Selby wrote to Jardine that he also had received a number and that 'Mrs. G. is improving every day in her drawing and attitudes'. Her birds were accurately, carefully and precisely delineated; Elizabeth Gould's delicate work has a quiet, pristine charm compared to the sophistication of later Gould prints. The birds still retain some of the stiffness of isolated specimens perched on tree stumps, branches or mounds — backgrounds which were merely uncoloured props, although a few trial prints do exist with coloured backgrounds. Edward Lear claimed that he began his association with Gould by assisting 'Mrs. Gould in all her drawings of foregrounds', but the tight drawing of most of these prints shows little evidence of his flowing line.

Gould intended to limit the number of copies of his work to about 200 subscribers — the price when first published of each section with four plates was 12 shillings, later, complete with text, £14.14s. — and then destroy the stones to make his work 'more scarce and consequently sought after'. The subscribers mentioned in *A Century of Birds from the Himalayas* eventually numbered 298, (although 332 are mentioned in Gould's published 1870 list of overall subscribers, when no copies of the Himalayan birds remained) and the work was dedicated to King William IV and Queen Adelaide. Nicholas Aylward Vigors, Secretary of the Zoological Society, supplied the separate text which described the birds (including a sunbird called *Aethyopyga gouldiae* after Mrs. Gould), and presented six papers on Himalayan birds

Eagle Owl (Bubo maximus), a lithograph by Edward Lear, signed 'E Lear del', for Gould's 'Birds of Europe' 1. Lear depicted several owls for Gould; later, in his comic drawings, he often caricatured himself as one. (Osberton Trust)

to the Zoological Society. In 1831 at the first meeting of the British Association for the Advancement of Science at York, those attending could view not only an exhibition of drawings for 'Mr. Audubon's great work on American Ornithology', but also a display by Gould of the Himalayan specimens and copies of his work.

The success of the hundred Himalayan birds gave Gould the confidence to plan a much larger publication, *The Birds of Europe*, for which he issued a prospectus in October 1831. The first part appeared in June 1832 and the last in 1837. The edition, to be bound by the subscriber in five volumes, eventually numbered 448 plates in 22 parts, the average part having 20 plates and costing £3. A text was planned to appear with the plates, a scheme Gould used for all future works. To study the latest specimens Gould travelled abroad, accompanied by Elizabeth Gould or Edward Lear, to zoos and collections in Berlin, Amsterdam, Rotterdam and Berne. On one visit he borrowed specimens from the venerable Professor Conrad Temmick, Director of Leyden Musuem, taxidermist and author of lavish hand-coloured engraved books, whose house was almost entirely filled with stuffed birds. Lear, who was delicate in health and suffered from asthma and epilepsy, complained about these journeys in later years, and he must have found it difficult to cope with Gould's restless personality and demanding ways. His contribution, 68 plates, was mostly of larger birds – the owls, crane, pelican, swans, purple heron and sea eagle. The remainder were drawn by Mrs. Gould. Although Gould acknowledged Lear's work in the Preface, some of Lear's illustrations, such as the barn owl, cinereus vulture, and great auk which are clearly signed 'E. Lear' on the plate, bear an attribution to 'J. & E. Gould' in the inscription underneath. Sometimes Lear's signature appears purposely large, as if to ensure that his name could be seen even if the printers added the wrong credit lines afterwards! Lear must have been annoyed by these discrepencies, but it is likely that Gould, in his constant rush to publish, overlooked these errors, rather than deliberately misrepresented Lear's work.

The most memorable Lear plates are of owls and pelicans, sometimes drawn so large as almost to overwhelm the page. He was short-sighted, suffering

Sea Eagle (Haliaectus albicilla), *a drawing in pencil, ink and watercolour by Edward Lear, a preliminary study for Gould's 'Birds of Europe' 1. Many pencilled notes with colour instructions have been written by Lear himself.*
(Blacker-Wood Library, McGill University, Canada)

The finished plate. (Osberton Trust)

from eye-strain, and in later years sometimes likened himself to an owl, recalling a little girl's comment 'how exactly your spectacles make you look like a big owl'. Although he had been commissioned to illustrate for Gould's *Birds of Europe* and the *Family of Toucans*, he also worked for Lord Stanley, later 13th Earl of Derby, a dedicated collector of rare animals and birds, in the superb private menagerie at Knowsley Hall near Liverpool. It was there that he entertained the children, grandchildren and great-grandchildren of the elderly 12th Earl, with the puns, riddles, funny drawings and humorous verse which were printed in *A Book of Nonsense* in 1846.

While the *Birds of Europe* was in progress, Gould was accumulating skins of Toucans and Trogons from European collections and South American travellers. The large-billed, fruit-eating toucans, with their colourful bodies, made splendid illustrations. Their surprising variety of names, such as 'lemon rumped', 'sulphur and white breasted', 'saffron', and 'red billed' show that the orange and black bird, made familiar through *Guinness* advertisments, is not the only sort of Toucan found in tropical forests! These unusual birds needed to be depicted with great accuracy so that all the scientific differences could be recognised. But they also had to appear realistic and

Toco Toucan (Ramphastos toco), *a lithograph by Edward Lear, signed 'E Lear del 1833', for Gould's 'A monograph of the family of toucans' (1833-5). Gould described this species as the largest of the toucans and remarkable for its disproportionate bill.* (Osberton Trust)

lively – even though drawn from mounted skins. Tropical plants were added as backgrounds, which may have been studied at Kew, and sometimes pairs of toucans were shown, with one bird nesting in a tree trunk, making an attractive composition. Ten plates of the first edition of the *Family of Toucans*, (1833-1835, 34 plates), were signed and inscribed as by Edward Lear, some dated 1833; the remainder were attributed to 'J. & E. Gould'. Gould added further plates in a supplement in 1855, and a second edition in 1852-1854 had plates by H.C. Richter.

At Knowsley menagerie, in July 1836, Lear painted a beautiful Toco Toucan (*Ramphastos toco*) with meticulous finish and detail. Later that year, in October, he complained of the strain of this precise zoological work on his sight and wrote to Gould that his eyes were 'so sadly worse, that no bird under an ostrich should I soon be able to see to do'. It was perhaps as a relief from this exacting work that he indulged in doodling funny pictures of owls, pelicans, parrots and cranes to amuse and delight his friends.

Elizabeth Gould, assisted by Edward Lear, worked on the *Family of Trogons*, (36 plates, all ascribed to J. & E. Gould) which appeared in parts from 1835. These exotic birds were almost as colour-

Chestnut-eared Aracari (Pteroglossus castanotis), *a drawing in pencil and watercolour attributed to John Gould. This rough study, similar to the first edition plate in Gould's 'Monograph of Toucans', was used again as a composition for Richter's lithograph of the Curl-crested Aracari (Pteroglossus beauharnaisi) in the 2nd edition. (Spencer Library, University of Kansas)*

Red-billed Toucan (Ramphastos erythrorhynchus), *a drawing in pencil, ink, watercolour and tempera by Edward Lear for Gould's 'Monograph of Toucans' first edition (1833-35), a close study for the final plate. Gould described this toucan as being distinguished by the brilliant colouring of its beak.*
(Blacker-Wood Library, McGill University, Canada)

Black-mandibled Toucan (Ramphastos ambiguus), *a drawing in pencil and watercolour attributed to John Gould for the second edition of the 'Monograph of Toucans' (1852-4). This rough compositional sketch is a study for the finished plate, but further greens and blues were added to the bills, and round the bare skin of the eye. (Spencer Libarary, University of Kansas)*

ful as the toucans, but more graceful. The male quetzal had such a long resplendent tail that a double folded page was needed to accommodate it. In the second edition (1858-1875), William Hart instead drew the quetzal with his tail curled up. (Below)

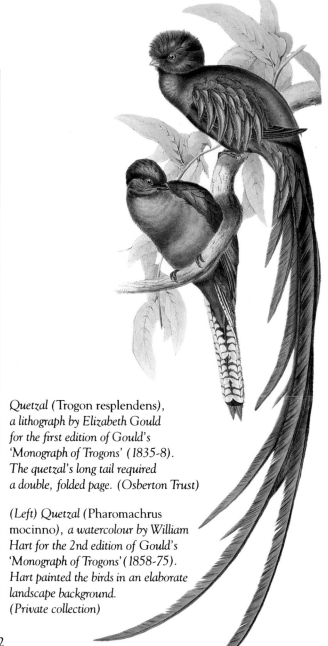

Quetzal (Trogon resplendens), *a lithograph by Elizabeth Gould for the first edition of Gould's 'Monograph of Trogons' (1835-8). The quetzal's long tail required a double, folded page. (Osberton Trust)*

(Left) Quetzal (Pharomachrus mocinno), *a watercolour by William Hart for the 2nd edition of Gould's 'Monograph of Trogons' (1858-75). Hart painted the birds in an elaborate landscape background. (Private collection)*

Elegant or Graceful Trogon (Trogon elegans), a drawing attributed to Gould in pencil and watercolour for the second edition of the 'Monograph of Trogons' (1858-75). This was a compositional experiment; the final plate (right) shows two cock birds in the foreground, a small hen bird in the background among the leaves. (Spencer Library, University of Kansas)

The finished plate. (Osberton Trust)

Plans were in progress for a Gould book about Australian birds when Edward Lear decided to give up his demanding zoological commitments and take up landscape painting, a task he hoped would be less exacting. In July 1837 he left England for Rome, to a warmer climate, hoping to avoid winter colds and bronchitis. Gould missed his illustrator, but Lear wrote from Rome 'I am and have been going on very well, which is more than ever I had a right to expect, in spite of your good opinion of me: I am very glad I took to Landscape.' Except for occasional visits to England, and one stay from 1849-1853, he remained abroad, producing travel books of Italy, Albania, Corsica and Greece, and died at San Remo in Italy in 1888. Lear wrote friendly, chatty, letters from Rome, thanking the Goulds for 'many kindnesses of days gone' and longing to have 'an immense talk'. In old age Lear recalled unhappy memories, for he wrote after Gould's death in 1881 'He was one I never liked really, for in spite of a certain jollity, and bonhommie, he was a harsh and violent man. At the Zoological Society at 33 Bruton Street, at Hullmandels, – at Broad Street ever the same, persevering hard working toiler in his own (ornithological) line'. Lear in his last years was often crabbed and lonely, and a more amusing recollection is Lear's jovial invitation asking Gould to visit Rome in 1844: 'I can give you a spare bed if you like to put up with the roughness and fleas and porcupines flesh and snails for dinner . . . Good wine though. Come'.

Barn Owl (Strix flammea), a lithograph by Edward Lear for Gould's 'Birds of Europe' I. Signed 'E. Lear. del' but with the inscription attributed to 'J. & E. Gould'. (Osberton Trust)

44

Chapter 5 *Circumnavigating the Globe*

Before the Goulds' plans for the work on the *Birds of Australia* came to fruition, John Gould became involved in a co-operative project with another scholar. On October 2nd 1836 Charles Darwin arrived back in England on the ship *H.M.S. Beagle*, after travelling round the world for nearly five years. He had accumulated a large and curious collection of preserved birds, animals, rocks, shells, and insects, and needed expert help in their description and identification for his production of the *Zoology of the Voyage of H.M.S. Beagle,* (five volumes 1838-1841), towards which he was granted £1000 from the British government. Darwin had heard of Gould's books from Thomas Campbell Eyton, a naturalist friend from Cambridge days who had bought the Toucan prints. They were expensive, he wrote, but of good value as he had since been offered a higher price! Through the Zoological Society, Charles Darwin initially made contact with John Gould about a special Rhea, seen during his travels in Northern Patagonia. This Rhea was an ostrich of dark, mottled colour, with legs which were shorter and feathered lower than the Common Rhea. Conrad Martens, the artist on the Beagle expedition, shot one for food and it was cooked and eaten before Darwin realised that it was not simply an undergrown ostrich, but another less-known species. Fortunately the head, neck, feathers and skin had been preserved, and were sent to the Zoological Society, where it was put together, and a nearly perfect specimen made for display. Gould classified the Rhea as a new species, which he called Darwin's Rhea, *Rhea Darwinii*, and later Darwin presented a paper about their discovery to the Zoological Society.

The third volume of the *Zoology of the Voyage of H.M.S. Beagle,* containing fifty plates of birds, was advertised by Darwin as 'taken from sketches made by Mr. Gould himself, and executed on stone by Mrs. Gould'. It is the only volume of Gould's works in which all the illustrations are by the Goulds themselves, and Darwin's description clearly shows the role that each took in their very exact partnership.

When Gould and Darwin were examining the birds brought from the Galapagos Islands, they were fascinated by a group of about thirteen finches of the same species, which had curiously different-sized beaks – some as large as a hawfinch, others as small as a warbler. These modifications occurred on different islands, and it was the investigation of this, and other scientific data accumulated over a long period, that led to Darwin's theories of evolution by adaption formulated many years later. Frank Sulloway (Harvard University 1982), has investigated Gould's part in Darwin's theory of evolution, and shows that Gould astutely realised the basic peculiarites of these birds, thus paving the way for Darwin's first notes on the 'Transmutation of Species'. Gould presented descriptions of the Galapagos finches and mockingbird specimens at the Zoological Society in January 1837. But he was unable to finish his work for Dar-

Large-beaked Finches (Geospiza strenua) *from the Galapagos islands, a lithograph for Darwin's 'Zoology of the Voyage of H.M.S. Beagle' by John and Elizabeth Gould. These finches greatly interested both Gould and Darwin, and contributed to Darwin's evolutionary theories. (Osberton Trust)*

win. Due to the hurry and rush before the Goulds' departure to Australia, parts of his manuscript were left unresolved, and the work was completed by George Robert Gray of the British Museum.

For several years Gould had been excited by descriptions and specimens of Australian birds sent by his brothers-in-law in New South Wales. In 1837-1838 he illustrated some of these birds in a small book *Synopsis of the Birds of Australia*, mostly of birds heads, and started two parts (20 plates) of the imperial folio volumes of his formidable enterprise *The Birds of Australia*. (These parts, now known as the 'cancelled parts', were recalled by Gould from subscribers after his return from Australia, in exchange for parts in a revised series. He rightly prophesied that the cancelled parts, not all of which were returned, would 'some day be of value . . . more to the Book Collector, than the Naturalist'). But in spite of all his commitments in London, Gould decided he must delay no longer, and explore the new continent for himself before other ornithologists arrived on the scene. So he planned to use his earnings – he was reputed to have made £7,000 from his books – towards a two year expedition to Australia.

Elaborate preparations had to be made at home and for the journey. Gould relinquished his post at the Zoological Society, and handed over his financial affairs and the running of the taxidermist business to the indispensable secretary Mr. Edwin Prince. In order to keep busy on board ship Gould had a cabin on the sailing barque *Parsee* fitted out for work with birds and books. Mrs. Gould, as his illustrator, needed to travel with him – but perhaps she was able to have some rest from 'drawing on stone' when at sea! She was sad about leaving their small children – the three youngest were left in the care of her mother and married niece – but their eldest son Henry, aged 7, went with them as well as a nephew, two servants and John Gilbert, a collector and explorer employed by Gould. 'I am so busy that my brain is in a complete jumble' Gould wrote to Sir William Jardine. The 'American Woodsman', Audubon, wrote wryly about Gould's new venture to his friend John Bachman, in America: 'Mr. Gould . . . is about leaving this country for New Holland, or as it is now called Australia. He takes his wife and Bairns with him, a Waggon the size of a Squatters Cabin, and all such apparatus as will encumber him not a little – he has never travelled in Woods, never salted his rump stakes with Gun Powder and how he will take to it, will be a sin to Crocket.' 'Davy' Crockett was Audubon's hero, but Gould, although perhaps not a hardened 'frontierman', was nevertheless an expert shot!

The four-month journey to Tasmania, May to September 1838, proved safe, although on her next passage between Hobart and Adelaide the *Parsee* was totally wrecked, fortunately with no lives lost. Gould was anxious to testify that Captain McKellar had been careful, strict, and in perfect command during their voyage. He been grateful to the captain for allowing him to use the ship's boat and dinghy, lowered into the sea during calm weather to observe and even ring some ocean birds.

In Tasmania, the Goulds were looked after by the Governor, Sir John Franklin (of Arctic fame) and Lady Franklin, who were greatly interested in the flora and fauna of the country. The dynamic Lady Franklin, in six years on the island, started a Museum, a botanical garden, a 'Tasmanian Journal of Science'; in 1840 a small natural history society was founded, later the Royal Society of Tasmania, which admitted women and was the first society of its kind in the colonies. With Gould she eagerly organised a group expedition by the government schooner to the south coast of the island and Recherche Bay, which was not completely successful due to bad weather, and contributed towards other journeys in Northern Tasmania and Flinders Island.

Franklin Gould as a child, a pencil and pastel portrait attributed to John Gould. Franklin was born in Hobart in 1839. His mother wrote proudly: 'this little Tasmanian is a prodigious fellow – everyone says so'. (Private collection)

Meanwhile Mrs. Gould sketched plants and was given hospitality at Government House during the birth of her fifth child to survive infancy, christened Franklin Tasman Gould, who soon became a 'great pet with all the family'. Later, Lady Franklin, herself childless, thought of adopting the him, but Elizabeth refused to part with her 'little Tasmanian'.

A Tasmanian plant, drawn in watercolour by Elizabeth Gould while staying at Government House in Hobart when her husband was away exploring Tasmania and South Australia. It is inscribed 'Richea dracophylla' and 'VD Land'. (Private Collection)

Australian heron (Ardea leucophaea), a drawing attributed to John Gould for Richter's plate in 'Birds of Australia' VI.

Elizabeth Gould wrote home in 1839: 'Many of the birds possess very curious habits. I think the mass of information John has obtained cannot fail to render our work highly interesting to the scientific world'. Gould constantly exclaimed on the beauty of these 'novelties', the parakeets and honeyeaters, or the 'curious habits' of the bower-birds and lyre-birds, and although engrossed by ornithology could not fail to notice extraordinary mammals such as the platypus, spiny echidna, wombats or koalas. Copious notes were made and John Gilbert, whom Gould employed at £100 per year plus expenses, remained in Australia to add vital information from journeys in Western Australia. Gilbert made further explorations to the Northern Territory, but during an overland expedition in 1845 with Ludwig Leichardt from Brisbane to Port Essington, was tragically killed by aborigines. His notes are written on some of Gould's manuscripts about Australian birds which are in the Balfour and Newton Library, Cambridge.

'Why do you appear to walk topsy-turvy so long?' wrote Lear from Rome, in October 1839. 'When you come back, you will all be puzzled to walk properly'. Gould apparently did not appreciate Lear's long and amusing letters, for Lear wrote that in three years he had received merely a short scrawl 'only one word of which out of every 2d can I decipher'. He asked that Mrs. Gould should act as secretary, and he would keep Gould's 'last and only epistle to see if I can't sell it as an ancient hieroglyphic'. A further half-sad,

Three stages in the development of a Gould print: the rough compositional sketch of bower-birds by John Gould himself ; a fine watercolour, possibly by H.C. Richter; and (right) the hand-coloured finished lithograph, never published. (Dr Gordon C. Sauer)

half-jocular letter talked of marriage. 'I wish to goodness I could get a wife! . . Please make a memorandum of any lady under 28 who has a little money – can live in Rome and knows how to cut pencils and make puddings.' Was 'the pencil-cutting pudding-making lady' based on a memory of Mrs. Gould?

On their return in August 1840, the Goulds, having circumnavigated the globe, soon set to action, for by December part 1 of the new series of the *Birds of Australia* was due to appear. Their living, tame birds from Australia – the vigorous budgerigars and some 'pretty singing New South Wales parrots' – were a great social success both at scientific meetings and fashionable parties. Gould was delighted when Prince Albert expressed interest in them at Lord Northampton's evening soirée, and expected the Queen might soon ask to see the 'little pets' too.

In the summer of 1841, Gould took a cottage in Egham, on the Thames, where he could fish, his favourite hobby, and still be accessible to London. The family would get some country air, as a change from their home in Broad Street, Soho, an area often threatened by cholera. But tragically, in August, Elizabeth Gould died of puerperal fever, following the birth of her eighth child (the sixth to live past infancy). She was only 37 and her death was a severe shock to her husband. Throughout his life Gould

Spotted Bower-bird (Chlamydera maculata), *an unusual double-page lithograph by H.C. Richter for 'Birds of Australia' IV. Gould was fascinated by the habits of the bower-bird; this species decorates its 'place of rendezous' with white, pale or reflective objects.* (Osberton Trust)

paid heartfelt tribute to her memory, and in the *Handbook to the Birds of Australia* (1866), expressed his feelings of 'purest affection for my late wife, who for many years laboriously assisted me with her pencil, accompanied me to Australia, and cheerfully interested herself in all my pursuits'.

It was now necessary for Gould to find another lithographer who could interpret his sketches and Mrs. Gould's drawings to make the remaining illustrations of the *Birds of Australia*. One plate, the emu and chicks, was contributed by Benjamin Waterhouse Hawkins, who also lithographed 16 plates of specimens from explorations along the coast of America and the Pacific Islands, for Gould in the bird section of *The Zoology of the Voyage of H.M.S. Sulphur* (1843-1844), and later made the cement monsters of extinct animals at Crystal Palace. But the person who filled Elizabeth Gould's place as illustrator was the young Henry Constantine Richter (1821-1902), a devoted worker, who remained with Gould for nearly forty years and contributed over a thousand prints.

Almost nothing was known about H.C. Richter until Mrs. Christine Jackson published a carefully researched account of his life in the *Journal of the Society of Bibliography: Natural History, 1978.* H.C. Rich-

Swift Lorikeet (Lathamus discolor), a watercolour painted by Elizabeth Gould during her stay at Government House in Tasmania for her lithograph in 'Birds of Australia' V. The plant is the local tree Eucalyptus gibbosus, whose thick clusters of pale yellow blossom provide honey for the birds. It is interesting to see that the birds are positioned 'upside down' in the finished plate. (Private collection)

The finished plate. (Osberton Trust)

54

ter was twenty years old when he first worked for Gould and had made some lithographs for George Robert Gray's *Genera of Birds* (1844-49). He was descended from an artistic family. His grandfather, an engraver, artist and scagliolist, had come from Germany and his father, Henry James Richter was a noted historical painter, engraver, and President of the Associated Artists in Water-Colours 1811-1812. His sister, Henrietta Sophia Richter, painted miniature portraits, which were exhibited at the Royal Academy from 1842 to 1849. H.C. Richter does not seem to have had other artistic ambitions – perhaps he lacked incentive, or was overshadowed by his family or employers. His work was that of a formal accomplished draughtsman, a careful conscientious artist who was the perfect interpreter of Gould's ideas for the finished prints. In his will Gould left 'my artist H_____ C_____ Richter' £100 for the purchase of a memento in memoriam – the entry with blank spaces left after the initials for the full Christian names could imply that Gould was still on formal terms, even though he had employed the man for nearly forty years! Richter died, a bachelor aged 81, his name little remembered, eleven years after Gould in 1902, leaving some property and £200.

View of a wood in Van Dieman's Land by Simpkinson de Wesselow. Painted near Hobart in a fern-tree glade between 1844 and 1848, this view illustrates the landscape of the young colony at the time of Gould's visit. (Victoria and Albert Museum)

The Father of Australian Ornithology
Allan McEvey

*T*he *Birds of Australia* by John Gould has been described by Kenneth Hince as one of the world's finest books, probably the most valuable and desirable of all printed works relating to Australia.

There is indeed a nineteenth century grandeur about this work that was, in some ways, Gould's greatest. A few lines from Gould to the Scottish naturalist Sir William Jardine in 1836 possibly represent its genesis: . . . 'Would not a work on the Birds of Australia be interesting? I have a great number of new and interesting species to make known and have an idea of making it my next illustrative work'. A manuscript in the Balfour and Newton Library in Cambridge entitled 'General List of Birds inhabiting Australia and the adjacent islands' is clearly a basic working list prepared by Gould for his Australian project.

In 1837-8 Gould published *A Synopsis of the Birds of Australia and the Adjacent Islands* to record and illustrate new Australian species. Concurrently there appeared *The Birds of Australia and the Adjacent Islands* (1837-8), cancelled after two parts and now known as the 'Cancelled Parts'. The first part of *The Birds of Australia* appeared in its final form in 1840.

The years 1838-40 were spent by the Goulds in Australia gaining field experience with the Australian avifauna. John and Elizabeth Gould, Henry, their seven-year old son, Henry Coxen, their nephew aged fourteen, two servants and John Gilbert, the zoological collector, left England on 16th May, 1838.

At Hobart in Tasmania, reached four months later, the Goulds' headquarters were at 'old Government House'. Gould himself and Gilbert explored the Derwent River-Macquarie Plains area, Recherche Bay and its islands, the George Town-Tamar River area, and then Bass Strait islands. Meanwhile Elizabeth, befriended by the Governor's

Pied Grallina (Grallina Australis), known as Magpie Lark (Grallina cyanoleuca). The name Grallina used by Gould has been retained for this very small group of birds. (Osberton Trust)

wife, Lady Franklin, began her work of preparing drawings of birds and plants.

In February 1839 Gilbert was sent to Swan River, Perth, where he collected for eleven months before travelling to Sydney. Gould himself sailed to Sydney and then, from the homestead of Elizabeth Gould's brothers at Yarrundi, near Scone, carried out his field work in the Hunter River-Liverpool Ranges area, returning to Hobart in April 1839. By then he is recorded as having gathered about 800 specimens of birds, 70 of quadrupeds, and nests and eggs of more than 70 species of birds, together with skeletons of all the principal forms.

In June he began a journey with Captain Sturt, the Surveyor General, from Adelaide to 'the Murray Scrubs' (the Mallee), returning to Adelaide in July, from where he visited Kangaroo Island, before returning to Hobart. The family left Tasmania for Sydney in late August, and during September travelled via Newcastle up the Hunter River to Maitland and then by cart to Yarrundi, where Elizabeth continued to prepare sketches while Gould studied in the nearby forests and the eastern slopes of the Liverpool range. Then followed 'his most ambitious and successful expedition through sparsely-settled country,' K.A. Hindwood writes.

'The party consisted of five Europeans and two . . . aborigines, Natty and Jemmy, whom Gould termed his 'faithful companions' and whose knowledge of wild life and bushcraft he found very helpful. Apart from his first visit to Yarrundi . . . Gould spent some four months in the Upper Hunter-Liverpool Range-Namoi area'.

After returning to Sydney in February 1840 Gould visited Illawarra and then on April 9th the family, John and Elizabeth with their two sons (Franklin had been born in Tasmania), sailed for England, arriving in August 1840. They had been away for some twenty-seven months, during nineteen of which Gould had been actively studying the bird life of Tasmania and the adjacent islands, South Australia and New South Wales, and everywhere had received assistance from all sides, notably the Colonial Governors.

Elizabeth's contribution to the project was two-fold. First was the loving one of being with her husband while leaving three children in England. She was '. . . a warm and gentle person', as revealed

Crested Penguin (Eudyptes chrysocome), *drawn in pencil, chalk and wash, attributed to John Gould, for 'Birds of Australia' VII. (Spencer Library, University of Kansas) Inset: the finished plate (Osberton Trust)*

by her letters home asking her mother, for example, to 'Say everything that is kind to everybody on our part'. She also showed a pioneering fortitude in her separation from her children, writing 'Oh my dear Mother, how happy shall I be if permitted to see you once more and my dear children'; and again, 'I sigh and think if I could but see old England again, and the dear treasures it contains, I would contentedly sit down at my working table and *stroke, stroke* away to the end of the chapter, that is health permitting'.

And secondly came the essential contribution of producing drawings of birds and plants for later reference. However, only 84 of the 681 plates in *The Birds of Australia* carry her name in the legend; she died only a year after their return home.

What of Gould's own role and his historical place in relation to the ornithology of Australia? Gould's enterprise flourished in the era of extensive collecting of birds and the description of species. There is no doubt that he had a brilliant natural talent for the recognition of new species character in birds and therefore for the science of avian systematics (taxonomy) involved with describing and naming bird species. This he linked with both expertise in taxidermy and an ability to capture the field character of birds in rough sketches.

Yellow-collared Parakeet (Platycerus semitorquatus), drawn in pencil, ink and crayon, attributed to John Gould, for Richter's lithograph in 'Birds of Australia' V. Gould wrote that this bird 'deposits its eggs in the hole of the gum or mahogany tree'. (Spencer Library, University of Kansas)

The finished plate. (Osberton Trust)

The approach of Gould in systematics was straightforward. He no doubt learned from his association and correspondence with other naturalists and from reading, but his native talent enabled him to progress rapidly in the matter of describing and naming genera and species, chiefly in the Proceedings of the Zoological Society of London.

Gould, though not innovative, followed some leaders of contemporary thought in readily creating new genera; at the same time he showed respect for the law of priority in nomenclature, readily subduing his names when it was found that earlier ones existed. Although many of Gould's systematic placings and names in Australian ornithology have not been preserved by modern research, a remarkable number of his names *have* survived and some of the forms he found puzzling remain so today, the Magpie Lark *(Grallina cyanoleuca)* being an example. His work with specimens from all over the world gave him a perspective that few others possessed. The Australian systematists Mathews and Iredale, writing in 1938, spoke highly of Gould's judgement: 'his work as a systematist claims praise from every serious investigator after a century's trial'.

In addition to Gould's systematics, there are

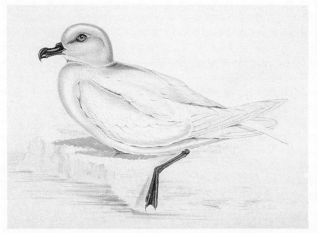

Short-tailed Petrel (Puffinus brevicaudus) *drawn in pencil and watercolour by Elizabeth Gould for 'Birds of Australia' VII. Inscribed 'Latt 39.22 S Long 57.55 W J&E Gould', it was probably painted during the voyage from Australia, April-August 1840, when Gould made a special study of petrels. (Spencer Library, University of Kansas)*

The finished plate (Osberton Trust)

The finished plate (Osberton Trust)

White-fronted Falcon (Falco frontatus), *drawn in pencil and watercolour, attributed to Elizabeth Gould, for 'Birds of Australia' I. It is interesting to compare this little falcon with the birds of prey illustrated by Lear and Wolf.*
(Spencer Library, University of Kansas)

other important aspects of his published works on Australian birds. Before Gould's works, drawings and notes on Australian birds from early voyagers had been published by Latham, White and others, and Lewin had published his *Birds of New Holland* in 1808. These, although of great importance, were of minor substance by comparison with the seven volumes of *The Birds of Australia* (1840-48), containing approximately 600 species and providing in its dignified prose a wealth of information gathered from wide sources. Thus, sixty years after the arrival of the First Fleet there was a truly major work, published by Gould himself, illustrating, and establishing the taxonomy of, the Australian avifauna. Nothing can detract from this gargantuan achievement that ranks highly in the world's ornithology.

This was not all however. Gould also published *A Monograph of the Macropodidae or Family of Kangaroos* (2 parts, 30 plates 1841-42) and *The Mammals of Australia* (3 vols., 182 plates 1845-63) both illustrated with hand-coloured lithographs. Gould's reason for undertaking such a task is found in the Preface to *The Mammals of Australia*: '. . . It was not . . . until I arrived in the country, and found myself surrounded by objects as strange as if I had

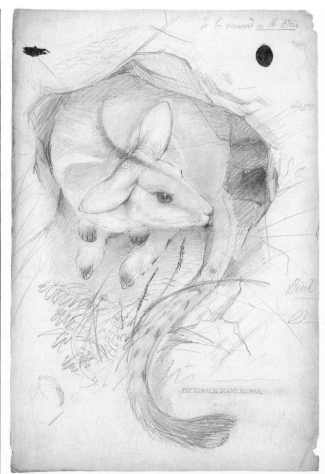

Yellow-footed Rock Wallaby (Petrogale xanthopus), *a pencil drawing attributed to Gould for Richter's lithograph in 'Mammals of Australia' II, with annotations in Richter's hand. Hunted for its soft fur, Gould urged its preservation through rearing in zoos. (Spencer Library, University of Kansas)*

been transported to another planet, that I conceived the idea of devoting a portion of my attention to the mammalian class of its extraordinary fauna'.

Gould's ability to turn from ornithology to make a major contribution in a separate field was astonishing. As Joan Dixon wrote in 1983 'It is remarkable that so many of these species have diagnostic features recognizable in the plates, and have been for me and for many others the only colour plates of some species available for identification purposes. For extinct or rare species this is particularly true. The value of Gould plates is inestimable, for colour and for their unique character.' 'The plates and the text are still referred to and used in modern works; the ideas which he discussed then are now more appropriately recognized'.

Thus Gould's contribution to the study of Australian mammals, though generalized in approach and not as extensive as that on birds, was no less significant or lasting, and again illustrates Gould's enormous energy, enterprise and ambition.

Finally, Gould's Australian works are a collection of fine books in natural history. The *Synopsis*, important for its information on nomenclature, contains 73 plates attributed to Elizabeth Gould, showing hand-coloured lithographs of heads of birds that are often of considerable appeal, as is the harmony of plate and typography. The 'Cancelled Parts', the rarest of Gould's works, is of special interest to the ornithological historian and to the collector. *The Birds of Australia* (7 vols., 1840-48) and its Supplement (1851-69) is a magnificent work. Its 681 hand-coloured lithographs represent the work of Elizabeth Gould (84 plates), Waterhouse Hawkins (1), Edward Lear (1) and H.C. Richter (595)many of which were probably based upon rough sketches by Gould, (information from the author's research notes).

Gould's role as inspirer and guide, and the propriety of the plates being known as Gould Plates, has been discussed by the author in 'John Gould's Contribution to British Art: A Note on its Authenticity' (Sydney University Press, 1973). At their best the plates are splendid examples of natural history illustration, attaining an artistic charm through the medium of the fine or original print. The *Handbook to the Birds of Australia* (1865), written as a 'careful résumé of the entire subject', reflects Gould's later and sounder understanding of zoogeography and provides the present-day worker

The finished plate. (Osberton Trust)

Great Red Kangaroo (Osphranter rufus), *drawn in pencil and watercolour by H.C. Richter for the 'Mammals of Australia' II. Richter drew studies of this splendid male, the most beautiful member of its family, at London's Zoological Gardens in 1853. Gould pleaded strongly for its protection against wanton killing by pasturalists in Australia. (Spencer Library, University of Kansas)*

with an invaluable link between the early and the recent.

On all counts, from demanding business practicalities, the hardships of expeditionary field-work and the production of a generally sound taxonomy for a new avifauna, to the gathering and publishing of vast new data in fine bird books, John Gould was indeed a monumental figure in, and is rightly called the Father of, Australian ornithology.

What of his productions on mammals of which, alone, any author would have been proud? Overawed by his energy and ability, what can we do but regard these as a rich and unexpected bonus!

© Allan McEvey

Author's note: Secondary sources, i.e. works by A.H. Chisholm, K.A. Hindwood, G. Sauer, Maureen Lambourne, Joan M. Dixon, other authors in *The Emu* Vol. XXXVIII part 2, pp.89-244, 1938, and A.R. McEvey, have been largely drawn upon for many aspects of this chapter.

In 'John Gould – Some Unanswered Questions', published in Books and Libraries at the University of Kansas 13:2, 1976, I sought the original source for the usual statement that 250 sets of *The Birds of Australia* were published. The source is page 2 of 'Prospectus of *The Birds of Australia*' bound in the octavo 'An Introduction to *The Birds of Australia* by John Gould, London: Printed for the Author 1848' stating, 'Only 250 copies have been printed, and the drawings have been effaced from the stones; . . .' (Copy in the Library of the Museum of Victoria.)   A.McE.

Chapter 6 *The Finest Points of the Bird . . . .*

The arrival of H.C. Richter, in 1841, and William Hart, in about 1851, to the Gould team set the pattern for the later productions, *The Family of Humming Birds* (5 volumes, 360 plates 1849-1861), *The Birds of Great Britain* (5 volumes, 367 plates 1862-1873), *The Birds of Asia* (7 volumes, 530 plates 1849-1883), and *The Birds of New Guinea* (5 volumes, 320 plates 1875-1888). For all publications Gould organised a Subscription List and usually a Prospectus, normal practice in the nineteenth century for luxury productions; and essential for Gould as he was his own publisher. The Prospectus, Gould's means of advertisement, was written in a heavy, Victorian manner – the announcement for the *Birds of Great Britain* began with typical pomp: 'The Author has been induced to commence this work at the urgent request of numerous persons taking great interest in our native birds . . .'. On several occasions Gould issued an impressive *List of Subscribers*,

to be sent with the prospectus of future works. The subscribers' names were compiled in order of social rank; the 1866 list started with Her Most Gracious Majesty Queen Victoria and the Prince Consort, the Emperor of Austria, and seven Kings of Europe. Libraries and Institutions were listed alphabetically, and locations, beginning with the Asiatic Society of Bombay and the Astor Library, New York, through the Academies of Philadelphia, St. Petersburg and Stockholm, and ending with the Zoological Society of London, show that Gould's work travelled throughout the world.

An account by John Gould's eldest daughter, Eliza, shows clearly her father's method of work in middle-age. After breakfast he was 'in his office, at the back of the house, busy with his books and birds, in all of which Mr. Prince was his help. Mr. Richter and afterwards Mr. Hart alone did the lithographing or drawing on stone from father's sketches and colouring from the same'. Some examples of Gould's 'sketches' are in carefully compiled notebooks of scraps, cuttings, letters and miscellaneous jottings for the *Birds of Great Britain*. Six of these books are in the Zoology Library of the Natural History Museum, London, and one in the Academy of Natural Sciences, Philadelphia. Under the title of each bird (carefully hand-written in Latin by Mr. Prince) is gathered information from friends, correspondents, naturalists, with their names carefully recorded as Gould was usually scrupulous, even monotonous, with acknowledgements in his text. Notes and sketches are made of specimens, acquired from skin-dealers, bird-catchers, gamekeepers, or killed by Gould himself, and their dimensions, weight and colour quickly recorded before fading or shrinkage set in.

Gould's quick drawings, in pencil, ink and broad colour wash, have directness, substantiality and a bludgeoning strength of character sometimes lost in the finished plates. They are often heavily annotated

The British Museum (Natural History) in London holds six man-uscript workbooks compiled by John Gould during preparation of the 'Birds of Great Britain' (1862-73). They contain notes, sketches, news clippings and correspondence and provide an invaluable insight into his method of working, as the following five illustrations show.

Green Woodpecker (Gecinus viridis). A drawing in pencil and wash by John Gould, dated '20 May 58', with annotations in three hands, in pencil: 'less black' (by Gould), 'stand up' (by H.C. Richter), 'bare swolen skin' (unknown hand). Instruc-tions, in ink, by Gould . . . 'all parts to be more neatly drawn'. British Museum (Natural History) sketchbook, Vol. 2, p. 22)

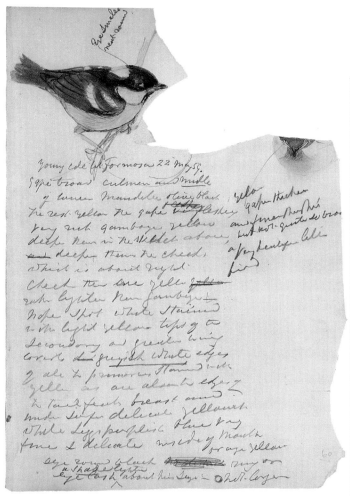

with colour notes and instructions, as if Gould, aware of his own artistic shortcomings, was anxious that all the finest points of the bird should be recorded. A typical scrawl annotates the young coal tit: '22 May 59 the gape fleshy, very rich gamboge yellow, deeper than in the sketch above, deeper than the cheeks which is about right . . '; the blue-throated warbler: 'the great beauty of this bird alive is the yellow at the base of the bill which contrasts strongly with the blue of the breast, and the black

Coal Tit (Parus ater). *A drawing in pencil and wash by John Gould, annotated 'Young cole tit Formosa 22 May 59'. A young bird has been cut away from this page, but the tit shows Gould's characteristic swift grasp of form. On the right are the remains of 'a very beautiful little bird', annotated by Gould 'yellow gape thicker'. Formosa Gardens, near Cookham on the Thames, was a favourite haunt of Gould.*
(British Museum (Natural History) sketchbook, Vol. 2 p. 60)

Young Robin (Erythacus rubecula), *drawn in pencil and water-colour by John Gould and annotated 'young robin June 5 Cliveden', (near Maidenhead). The claw is by another hand.*
(British Museum (Natural History) sketchbook, Vol. 3 p. 125)

Water-rail (Rallus aquaticus), *drawn in pencil, watercolour and pen attributed to H.C. Richter. It is annotated 'Male Osberton Jany 16 57' and 'Correct colours of the soft parts of the male (leg) when newly killed by me at Osberton' in Gould's hand.*
(British Museum (Natural History) sketchbook, Vol. 6 p. 34)

Little Grebe (Podiceps minor), *drawn in pencil and watercolour attributed to Richter, and annotated 'This grebe which was shot at Great Marlow on July 21st 57 . . .' by Gould in pencil and pen. The head is similar to the lithograph.*
(British Museum (Natural History) sketchbook, Vol. 7 p.136)

bill'. A sketch of a sand-martin's nest, 'July 4 '54', shows the lining made of swan's feathers, which 'curl round . . and all turn inwards like a tulip'. The scribbled 'young robin June 5. Cliveden' looks as if it was an impromptu drawing from life, and a quick pen sketch from memory, 'Nov 57', shows a water-rail strutting in the Zoological Gardens. Some, but not all, of these sketches, often dated but mostly unsigned, were used for the plates. Other finer

Common Guillemot (Uria troile), *drawing in pencil, watercolour and chalk, dated March 4th 1863. The rough sketchwork* is by Gould, *the fine drawing attributed to Richter.* (Spencer Library, University of Kansas)

Common Guillemot (Uria troile),
finished lithograph from his study (left),
by H.C. Richter in 'Birds of Great Britain' V.
(Osberton Trust)

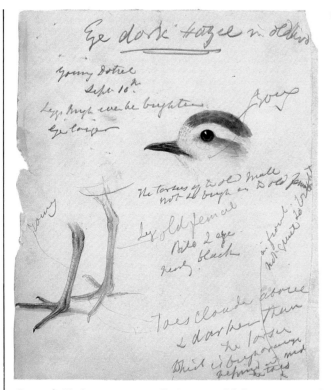

Dotterel (Eudromias morinellus), a careful drawing in pencil and watercolour, attributed to Richter and annotated by Gould: 'Young dotrel Sept 10th'. Drawn from a specimen in 1858. (British Museum (Natural History) sketchbook, Vol. 6 p. 67)

Dotterel (Eudromias morinellus), lithograph by Richter for 'Birds of Great Britain' IV. Gould's composition has been used, and Richter has added sheep on the downs to show where the dotterel migrate in summer. (Osberton Trust)

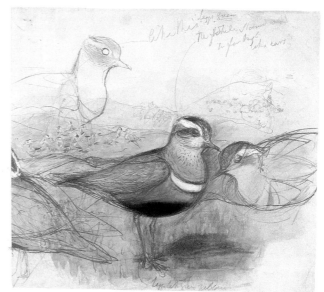

Dotterel (Eudromias morinellus), a rough composition sketch in pencil, watercolour and white gouache, by John Gould. The landscape is sketched in, and the birds have been heavily reworked in pencil over the wash and pencil drawing. Annotated by Gould: 'Like this' and 'The white stands out too far here like ears'. (Private Collection)

Quail and chicks (Coturnix communis), drawn in pencil and watercolour by John Gould as a sketch for the lithograph by H.C. Richter of the Common Quail in 'Birds of Great Britain' IV. The drawing is signed 'Quail J Gould 1863' and 'J Gould FRS March 11 1864', the second signature probably added when he gave the drawing to his friend Miss Marion Walker who sold it to the British Museum in 1890. (British Museum)

studies of bills and feet, and details added to the rough drawings, may be by another hand. A very good example of Gould's forceful style of drawing, and also his strong sense of composition, is the vigorous 'Quails and chicks', signed twice and dated March 11th 1864, a gift to his friend Marion Walker and now in the British Museum. It is a working study for the common quails of the *Birds of Great Britain*; in the finished plate Richter used Gould's broad grouping of the birds, but the large, clumsy, blue convolulus plant in the background was transformed into a dainty wood speedwell.

H.C. Richter and William Hart, thus guided by Gould's annotated sketches and composition 'workouts', and using specimens as models, or drawings from the Zoological Gardens – Richter made studies for kangaroos and mammals – finally made finished water-colour drawings for the plates. For the *Birds of Great Britain* Richter carefully arranged sprays of country flowers and wild blossoms as delicate coloured backgrounds for the demure English hedgerow birds; his sophisticated compositions showing the

Common Quail (Coturnix communis), the lithograph by H.C. Richter for 'Birds of Great Britain' IV. Richter has adapted Gould's rough drawing to show a dainty speedwell instead of a clumsy convolvulus. The quails are reversed. (Osberton Trust)

The finished plates, top row (Osberton Trust)

Robin (Erythacus rubecula) a watercolour study by H.C. Richter for his lithograph in 'Birds of Great Britain' II. Richter used the green ivy to enhance the rich red of the robin's breasts. (Private Collection)

Song Thrush (Turdus musicus), an exact watercolour study by H.C. Richter for 'Birds of Great Britain', II. (Private Collection)

Fieldfare (Turdis pilaris), an exact watercolour study by H.C. Richter for his lithograph in 'Birds of Great Britain' II, inscribed 'killed April 18th 1864'. John Box Esq., of White Place, Maidenhead, sent Gould these specimens of fieldfare shot by his keepers, and a drawing was made next day. Gould and Wolf had watched fieldfares nesting in Norway in the summer of 1856. (Private Collection)

song thrush amongst the dog rose, and the blackbird nesting in the honeysuckle, are masterpieces of balance and design.

The outlines from these finished drawings, with the bird's feathers, bill, legs and feet carefully delineated, were then, using tracing paper, drawn onto especially prepared stones hired from the printers. Hullmandel, in *The Art of Drawing on Stone*, described the use of tracing paper; the outline was traced with ink or pencil, soft red chalk or pencil was scored over, the tracing reversed and the outline carefully gone over with a blunt etching needle. According to Eliza Gould's description, Richter and Hart worked at Gould's own premises, 20 Broad Street, Soho, or, from 1859, 26 Charlotte Street, Bloomsbury. Each artist may have sat at a special desk, which could hold the heavy stones at a 45 degree slope, and used a wooden 'bridge' placed over the stone to avoid smudging the surface by the wrist or forearm. A hinged mirror, which appears in Hullmandel's diagrams of some desks, seems not to have been used, as the surviving finished drawings are usually, but not always, in reverse to the final plate. The completed stones were then sent to the printers; Hullmandel suggested they should be packed with the drawing upwards, and separated

Elegant pitta (Pitta concinna), was one of the many birds first described by Gould. The Ellis Collection in the Spencer Library, Kansas, has an almost a complete set of the many stages the picture passed through from original sketch to published lithograph, as the following five illustrations show.

Rough watercolour sketch, probably by Gould.

from each other by fixed wooden slips in special wooden carriers. Trial prints and proofs were taken and corrected, and a specialist in lettering (using mirror-writing) added title and attributions. The black and white prints were then ready for colouring. Hullmandel experimented with tinted printing, 'lithotint', but died in 1850, just before his trials were shown at the Great Exhibition. But Gould seems to have had no interest in any colour printing process, as all his plates were coloured by hand.

Specialists in hand-colouring usually worked in family groups at their homes, receiving batches of outline plates from the printers. They made their own 'pattern' prints based on the artist's finished drawing, and checked with the publisher that the colours were correct. Mr. Bayfield, and his assistants, are the colourists most frequently mentioned by name in Gould's notes and acknowledgements, and records of the Linnean Society show he lived at 14 Cadogan Street, and 25 Elizabeth Street, Chelsea. These records also show that a special colourist would receive between 3 pence and 9 pence a print, depending on the detail required.

Finally, the coloured plates and text would be placed into folders, which were carefully packed with boards in 'book boxes', to be sent away by coach or

Ink and watercolour drawing by Hart, annotated in pencil, possibly by Gould.

Transfer tracing, incorporating suggested changes.

Lithographic print, before the text was added, with pencil instructions, perhaps by Gould.

Final, hand-coloured lithograph as it appeared in 'Birds of New Guinea' IV. (Spencer Library, University of Kansas)

rail, or shipped abroad, usually twice a year. Instructions 'to the binder' were issued with the final part, for the intended finished order of text and illustrations varied substantially from the order in which they were sent. 'You cannot possibly bind my work on the *Birds of Great Britain* until it is finished, when titles, lists of plates, introduction, will be rendered . .' wrote Gould to an impatient subscriber, speaking of an edition which took eleven years to complete. Other publications were so protracted that some subscribers and Gould himself died before their completion – the *Birds of Asia* for example, published over a period of thirty-three years, was finished in 1883, two years after Gould's death, by Dr. Richard Bowdler Sharpe. The volumes became extemely heavy to handle – Lord Lilford wrote of the *Birds of Great Britain* 'you will find Gould's great work on that special subject in the Library, but the books are so large that you will require a boy to help you carry them from the house'. Gould's books were luxury productions which only the rich could afford, and many naturalists echoed William Swainson's hopes, never realised, that Gould would 'reprint these expensive volumes in such a form they may be accessible to naturalists: and thereby diffuse science, instead of restricting it to those only who are wealthy'.

The most inventive experiments by Gould's colourists were for the *Monograph of the Humming-Birds*, (360 plates, 1849-1861). Gould wished to capture on paper the irridescence of these jewel-like birds, and at the 1851 Great Exhibition, in the Fine Art Court, a display showed examples of Gould's humming-birds painted with transparent oil and varnish colours over pure gold leaf. He was in correspondence with William Baily of Philadelphia, who was also experimenting with metallic backgrounds for his books of watercolours of humming-birds, never published, and it was an occasion of great excitement when Gould visted Baily in America and saw his first living 'hummer' in Bartram's Gardens, Philadelphia, on 20th May 1857. But sadly some live humming-birds transported to England soon died, and Gould's plates were based on his large, comprehensive collection of stuffed specimens.

The year of the Great Exhibition of 1851, attracted crowds to London, and Gould used this opportunity to display his humming-birds in a specially built temporary house in the Zoological Gardens. Charging for exhibition was forbidden at the Crystal Palace in Hyde Park, where Gould's colouring process was demonstrated; but in Regent's Park, after negotiations with the Zoological Society,

A temporary building was erected in 1851 in the Zoological Gardens in London's Regent's Park to house Gould's exhibition of 1,500 stuffed humming-birds.
(Illustrated London News, 12th June 1852)

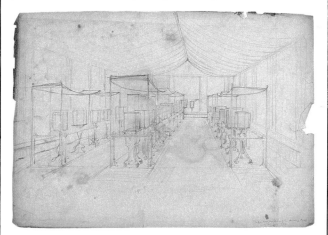

A design sketch in pencil, perhaps by John Gould, of the interior of the humming-bird exhibition house.
(Spencer Library, University of Kansas)

Over 75,000 visitors saw Gould's display of humming-birds, which were shown in special octagonal cases with canopies, designed to capture the birds' irridescent colours.
(Illustrated London News, 12th June 1852)

Gould was allowed to pay for erecting the building and receive the profits from a sixpence admission fee. Inside the pavilion the specially designed plate-glass cases, mostly octagonal, displayed the birds so that the irridescent colours could be seen from many angles, while canopies above the cases diffused the light.

The glittering display of 1500 humming-birds was immensely popular. Visitors in 1851 numbered about 75,000, and an extension was granted for the building to be re-erected in another part of the garden until the end of 1852. A small guide book was available for sixpence, and a visitor's book was left ready for the signatures of potential subscribers to Gould's series of imperial folio prints, the complete set of which, containing 350 plates, cost £78.15s.

From left to right: Green-headed Sapphire (Eucephala chlorocephala) and St. Domingo Humming-Bird (Sporadinus elegans). Lithographs by Richter for the 'Family of Humming-Birds' V. Many colour experiments were made to capture the glittering tones and irridescence of these birds. (Osberton Trust)

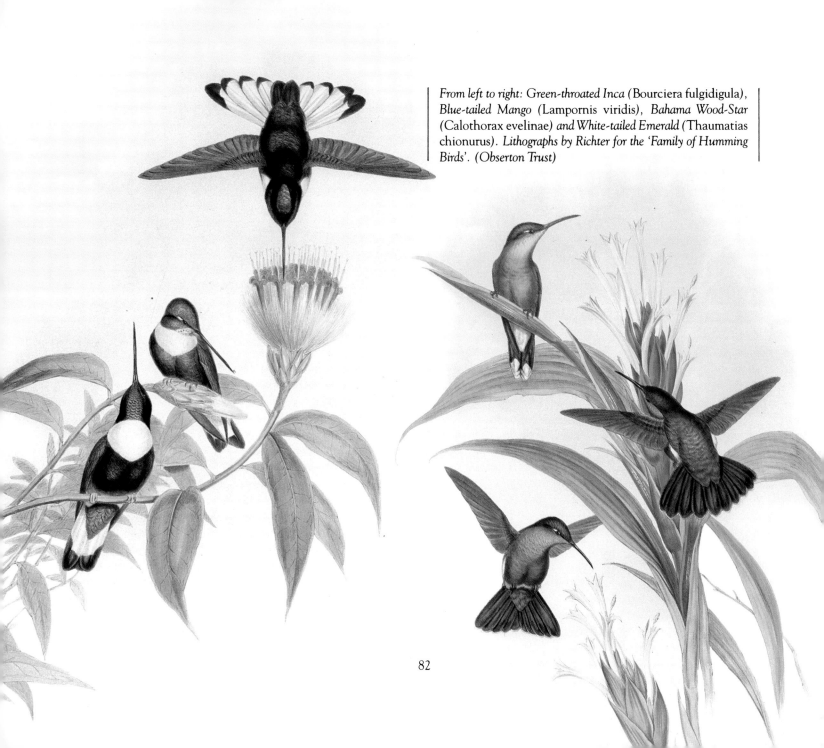

From left to right: Green-throated Inca (Bourciera fulgidigula), Blue-tailed Mango (Lampornis viridis), Bahama Wood-Star (Calothorax evelinae) and White-tailed Emerald (Thaumatias chionurus). Lithographs by Richter for the 'Family of Humming Birds'. (Obserton Trust)

From left to right: Blue-breast (Sternoclya cyaneipectus) and Shining sun-beam (Aglaeactis cupreipennis). The Shining sun-beam with its luminous purplish-crimson back was a favourite of Gould's. (Osberton Trust)

84

The Gould family moved to 26 Charlotte Street, Bloomsbury in October 1859. These unidentified birds have been drawn by different members of the family and annotated. 'From our garden at 26 Charlotte Street, Bedford Sq., April 6th '60'; 'Same state on 17th March 1868'. Further foliage was added by another hand and style in 'April 11th 1879'.
(Spencer Library, University of Kansas)

On 10 June 1851, Queen Victoria noted in her diary that she and Prince Albert drove with 'our three girls, Alexandrina and the 2 Ernests, to the Zoo,' to inspect 'a collection, (in a room specially designed for the purpose) of Gould's stuffed Humming Birds. It is the most beautiful and complete collection ever seen, and it is impossible to imagine anything so lovely as these little Humming Birds, their variety, and the extraordinary brilliance of their colours'. The cases of humming-birds also invaded Gould's drawing room, for his daughter Eliza describes how this attractively decorated room changed as 'father's collection of humming-birds grew larger, and he mounted fresh cases for want of other room', to become 'almost too full to move about. The housemaid was not allowed in it with broom or duster except on rare occasions, so in time it looked anything but pretty and of course was not used as a drawing-room'. The Prince of Wales and his brother visited 20 Broad Street, in May 1856, but on this occasion Gould showed them the birds which they could handle in his office, and the Princes 'took away with them two humming-bird's nests and eggs'. Three years later, when the Goulds moved to Charlotte Street, a special room was made for the humming-birds. After Gould's death 5,000 specimens

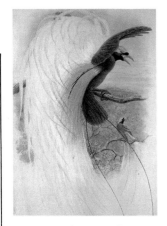   

Papuan Bird of Paradise (Paradisea papuana), a watercolour study by William Hart for 'Birds of New Guinea' (1875-88) I. (Private collection)   Finished plate (Osberton Trust)

Red Bird of Paradise (Paradisea sanguinea), a watercolour study by William Hart for 'Birds of New Guinea' (1875-88) I. (Private Collection)   Finished plate (Osberton Trust)

were bought by the Natural History Museum, and exhibited in sixty-two cases in 1886. Today a few octagonal cases with their original display still survive, and the birds, a little faded, have retained some of their original splendour through special preservation treatment.

William Matthew Hart (1830-1908) born in Limerick, Ireland, son of a water-colour artist of the same name, was Gould's artist for the *Supplement of the Humming-Birds* (1 volume, 58 plates 1880-1887), finished after Gould's death. Little is known of this fine artist, although like Richter he worked diligently for Gould. After beginning as a colourist on the early humming-bird plates, he lithographed several prints for the *Birds of Great Britain*. He worked as an artist

and lithographer for the later parts of the *Birds of Asia*, and for all the *Birds of New Guinea*, completed by Dr. Sharpe in 1888. His birds, especially the splendid birds of paradise, are broadly and fluently drawn, rich in colour, and set in elaborate backgrounds. Although he may have wished to be considered an artist rather than a draughtsman, he did not exhibit paintings and specialised in ornithological work. Unlike Richter, he was married with a large family to support – three sons and four daughters – living in various addresses in Walworth and Camberwell. John Gould in his will of 1878 left 'to my artist _____ Hart who has a large family' a legacy of £200; and a codicil of 1880 added a further £50 to this sum.

Papuan Bird of Paradise (Paradisea papuana), now Lesser Bird of Paradise, an oil painting on wood by William Hart. Similar in inspiration, but different in detail to the watercolour study and lithograph which appeared in 'Birds of New Guinea' (1875-88). Skins had been collected since the 18th century, but the first live Lesser Birds of paradise only arrived in England in 1862. (Sir David Attenborough)

Grey-chested Bird of Paradise (Paradisea decora), now known as Goldies' Bird of Paradise, an oil painting on wood by William Hart. Similar in design to the lithograph for 'Birds of New Guinea' I. Oil paintings by Hart are rare but oil was a medium well suited to the rich colours much loved by late Victorians. As neither Gould or Hart visited the Papuan Islands, the background is probably romanticised. (Sir David Attenborough)

The First Glittering Humming-Bird
Gordon C. Sauer

In John Gould's preface to his monograph on the humming-birds (*An Introduction to the Trochilidae, or family of humming-birds, 1861*) he wrote glowingly on 'my recollection of the first Humming-bird which met my admiring gaze! With what delight did I examine its tiny body and feast my eyes on its glittering plumage'. Humming-birds are species of birds of the Americas, and there were no live ones in England in the mid-1800's. Gould wrote further that 'my night dreams have not unfrequently carried me to their native forests in the distant country of America', and he was determined to see live humming-birds in their natural surroundings. His dreams were to be answered. In May 1857 John

Green-headed Emerald (Thaumatias Viridiceps). Lithograph by Richter for the 'Family of Humming-Birds' V. Gould saw his first live humming-bird in Philadelphia, and a group of fifty or sixty in Washington, 1856. A pair brought to England soon died, and the illustrations in his books are based on his unique collection of stuffed specimens. (Osberton Trust)

Gould and his son Charles embarked from Liverpool on the British Mail Steamer *Asia* bound for New York City.

The trip was to combine pleasure with business. Gould never travelled anywhere where he did not make some effort to obtain subscribers for his natural history works. This was an unceasing, frustrating, but fruitful labour. Secondly, he always sought out kindred naturalists with whom he could share notes on the 'natural economy' of birds. He was constantly exchanging specimens with other ornithologists so that he might make comparisons. The natural history network that John Gould established is very evident in the several thousand extant letters and notes that passed between him (with Edwin Prince as an amanuensis) and his many scientific colleagues, naturalist friends, subscribers (who of course were sometimes interested naturalists), and even his family. Gould has too often been depicted disparagingly as a successful business man. But one needs only to examine his notebooks and correspondence to be convinced that Gould was the all encompassing entrepreneur who combined many attributes. He was a naturalist, a taxidermist, a museum director, an artist, and a fantastic organiser.

In the pursuit of these endeavours, even before his trip in 1857, Gould's contacts in America had been extensive. As the 'curator and preserver' of the young, but even then prestigious, Zoological Society of London, Gould had first glance at many important, and frequently new, bird specimens. They were sent to the Society, and later to him personally, from all corners of the world. In his *Partridges of America* (1844-1850) Gould acknowledges the collections of the Scotsman David Douglas, who had travelled extensively in western North America.

Gould had frequent contact with Charles Lucian Bonaparte, who had lived in America. In 1838 Bonaparte had published a book comparing the bird species of Europe and North America, *A geographical and comparative list of the birds of Europe and North America*. For the European birds he used the colour plates from Gould's *Birds of Europe* as the 'Types of the Species' being considered, and for the North American he used the magnificent plates from John James Audubon's *Birds of America*. Bonaparte stated that 'Mr. Gould's work on the Birds of Europe, inferior in size to that of M. Audubon's, is the most beautiful work on Ornithology that has ever appeared in this or any other country'.

Gould's contacts with Audubon, when he resided in London, were quite numerous. They exchanged specimens and some publications. A definite sign of their friendship was the fact that Gould gave Audubon 'a *Pointer Bitch* of the finest *English blood* – I call her most beautiful – . . . her name is *Belle*, and she is a Belle indeed'. Audubon sent the dog by boat to his close friend Reverend John Bachman in Charlotte, South Carolina.

Gould was 52 years old when he travelled to America in 1857, six years after Audubon's death. He was already established as the most prominent British and Australian ornithologist, with an international reputation. In forty days he and his son visited New York City, Philadelphia, Washington, Cleveland, Buffalo, Niagara Falls (of course),

Plumed Partridge (Callipepla Picta), lithograph by Richter for 'A Monograph of Partridges'. Gould travelled extensively in Europe to find specimens for this monograph of the Ortyginae. (Osberton Trust)

Toronto, Montreal, Boston, New Haven, and then returned to New York City.

There are numerous items that corroborate the journey, where they visited, who and what they saw. Upon his arrival in New York City on the 16th of May, Gould wrote a letter to 'My dearest children . . . The entrance to New York from the sea is truly beautiful and from what I have seen of the place (I mean the City) I am not a little astonished and amused. I trust in a day or two to change this turmoil for quieter scenes in a state of nature . . .'.

In New York City Gould met George N. Lawrence, a prominent American ornithologist, with whom he exchanged humming-bird specimens. Lawrence in later years acted as Gould's subscription agent for America. Father and son then travelled to Philadelphia, and on the 19th of May John Gould was listed as being present at a meeting of the Academy of Sciences of Philadelphia. He had been elected a Corresponding Member of the society in 1843, shortly after his return from Australia. Dr. T.B. Wilson was in the chair, the man who, in 1847, had purchased for the Philadelphia Academy Gould's collection of over 1800 specimens of Australian birds, including many types, or first described specimens.

Gould had previously corresponded with another Philadelphian, William Baily, and when they met the young Baily took Gould to see a ruby-throated humming-bird in the famous Bartram's Gardens of Philadelphia. 'It was in his (Baily's) company that I first saw a living Humming-Bird in a garden which has become classic ground to all the Americans'. Also while in Philadelphia Gould made a pencil sketch of a bird which resembles the yellow-billed cuckoo. The notation (in Baily's hand?) on the drawing states 'Sketched by Mr. John Gould of London at this Academy May 1857'.

Gould and his son then travelled to Washington D.C. Here Gould saw more humming-birds, at one time fifty to sixty in a single tree. One bird was captured for him by some friends, which 'immediately afterwards partook of some saccharine food that was presented to it, and in two hours it pumped the fluid out of a little bottle whenever I offered it, and in this way it lived with me a constant companion for several days, travelling in a little thin gauzy bag distended by a piece of whale bone, and suspended to a button of my coat'.

Charles wrote a letter to the family from Boston, where they visited near the end of their stay, which included an itinerary of their previous stops. Here

Ecuadorian Tooth-bill (Androdon aequatorialis), *a drawing in pencil, ink and watercolour, attributed to William Hart, for his lithograph in the 'Supplement to the Family of Humming-birds' (1880-7). The pencil alterations are by Gould.*
(Spencer Library, University of Kansas)

The finished plate. (Osberton Trust)

we learn that in Washington 'pater familias dined with Lord Napier, and spent the evening with the President, the small boy was left at home upon each occasion'. Lord Napier was the new British Ambassador, and the President of the United States was Buchanan; but there is no further record of what should have been a memorable evening with the President. The 'small boy' left at home was 23 year old Charles.

One person in Washington of undoubtedly greater importance to John Gould was Spencer

93

Fullerton Baird, the Assistant Secretary of the Smithsonian Institution. There are fourteen extant communications between this ornithologist and Gould, including five letters written during Gould's American visit. They concern the exchange of bird specimens, and the request for live humming-birds for Gould to transport back to England.

Charles wrote in his Boston letter that 'we have been dashing over the country at such a rate that I have scarcely had time to think of you all at home.' Next on the journey after Washington was Cleveland, Ohio, where Gould met Dr Jared Kirtland; then to Buffalo where Gould met Mr Everard Palmer, a subscriber to several of his works. And then they proceeded to Niagara Falls. Charles was *not* disappointed in the falls; however, 'there being no Humming Birds in the neighbourhood, and no savants, Mr Gould found the beauty of the falls alone insufficient to attract him more than a few hours, so off we started again'.

The Canadian parliament was then in Toronto. Here Gould sold a complete set of his works, to be bound in the 'best manner' for the Library. Montreal was the next stop, where a note of his visit appeared in the Montreal Natural History Society Minutes of 1857: 'The Celebrated Ornithologist Mr Gould

F.R.S. . . . paid Montreal a flying visit of 3 or 4 days' around 6 to 9 June. And thence to Boston, where, Dr Cabot shared a new bird specimen with Gould. As a commemoration of the visit Gould, on his return to London, described the bird and named it *Ceriornis Caboti*.

A stop at Yale, and visits with librarian Edward C. Herrick and Professor James D. Dana, resulted in a subscription for Gould's humming-bird monograph; Gould in turn sent them a donation of 50 bird skins. Back in New York City Gould and Charles stayed at the Brevoort Hotel, until 24 June when they sailed on the Steamship *Kangaroo* for Liverpool. The vessel, Gould wrote, 'took a northerly course, which carried us over the banks of Newfoundland'.

John Gould's visit to North America was accomplished, but it did not end his correspondence and subscription sales to the Continent. These intensified, and Gould eventually had at least thirty subscribers to his works in the United States and Canada. Major subscribers were the Astor Library and R.L. Stuart of New York City, the Boston Society of Natural History, Dr. A. Binney of Boston, the Philadelphia Academy of Natural Sciences, and the Library of the Parliament of Canada.

Chapter 7 *A Ruling Passion*

Darwin's evolutionary theories created much controversy in the years after 1860, and gradually scientists turned away from classification and systematics to new biological research. Gould was remarkably unaffected by these changes, and his life maintained its normal pattern of working in his London office with skins, publishing his books, fishing and bird-watching by the Thames, shooting in Scotland, visiting country estates such as Osberton, and whirlwind trips to museums and collections abroad.

In his writings about 'instinct' in Chapter 8 of the *Origin of Species*, Darwin mentions Gould's description of the young cuckoo ejecting its foster-parents' chicks from the nest. Gould's account was based on the accurate observations and sketches of Mrs Hugh Blackburn, a water-colour artist, and wife of Professor Blackburn of Glasgow University. When writing about the cuckoo for the *Birds of Great Britain*, Gould had felt perplexed about how the cuckoo

Cuckoo (Cuculus canorus), *drawn by Mrs Hugh Blackburn (Jemima Wedderburn) from life on 22nd June 1860. The young cuckoo is expelling the meadow pipit's fledgling from the nest, and Gould amended his text after receiving a tracing of this drawing from the Duke of Argyll. A woodcut drawing and lithograph by Hart were added to the 'Birds of Great Britain'.*
(British Museum)

fledgling, only a few days old, could have the strength to eject other fledglings and had suggested that it was the foster-bird, tidying up the nest to make room for the cuckoo, who accidently caused the death of her own young. After he had published this text, he received from the Duke of Argyll a tracing of Mrs. Blackburn's drawing, which clearly showed the young cuckoo, with herculean strength, in the grisly act of ejecting some pipit fledglings out of their nest. Gould admitted his mistake, and had a diagram and lithograph made from Mrs. Blackburn's sketch to be inserted into his books. Darwin wrote that this 'strange and odious instinct' was, he felt, 'gradually acquired, during successive generations', a 'blind desire', similar to the instinct of unhatched young birds to break through their own shells into the world.

Gould found that writing about British birds was a welcome relaxation from his other work, as he could enjoy observing birds at the same favourite fishing haunts by the Thames that he had known as a youth. The artist Joseph Wolf recounted 'Gould was a most restless fellow, who would never sit down except when he was at Maidenhead when he would sit for hours'. Many anecdotes about Gould's burly character, usually jibes at Gould's expense, are

White Greenland Gyrfalcon (Falco rusticolus) on a gloved fist. This watercolour, by Joseph Wolf, belonged to Gould. It was made for the lithograph in Schlegel and Wulverhorst's 'Traité de Fauconnerie' (1844-53), a series of magnificent life-size illustrations which formed Wolf's first important commission before his arrival in England. (Private Collection)

related by A.H. Palmer, son of the painter Samuel Palmer, in his biography of Joseph Wolf, written in 1895. Wolf was a powerful animal painter and lithographer whom Gould eagerly sought as an illustrator for his books. Although Wolf contributed 57 plates to the *Birds of Great Britain*, and 24 plates to the *Birds of Asia*, he was not happy working for Gould and preferred to be free to paint his own 'subject' pictures rather than be committed to routine work.

Joseph Wolf (1820-1899) was, like Gould, brought up as a country boy and from an early age had a passion for birds and animals. He was born in the Rhineland, and when 16 was apprenticed to a commercial lithographic firm. But his interest was always in portraying wild life; and he eventually had the opportunity of making life-size falconry prints for Schegel and Wulverhorst's *Traité de Fauconnerie* (1844-53). These magnificent plates were much admired, and Gould later owned the majestic watercolour study, made for the book, of the hooded White Greenland Falcon. Wolf then decided to train in oil-painting, first at Darmstadt and then at Antwerp Academy, but political unrest overtook Europe in 1848, and he left for London, to accept a commission to make the last scientific illustrations for George Robert Gray's *Genera of Birds*.

Greenland Gyrfalcon (Falco candicans), *an exact watercolour study signed by Joseph Wolf, 1856 for Richter's lithograph in 'Birds of Great Britain' I. Wolf depicted these birds with unusually light plumage silhouetted against the blue sea and sky.* (Private Collection)

97

Icelandic Gyrfalcon (Falco islandicus), *an exact watercolour study by Joseph Wolf, for Richter's lithograph in 'Birds of Great Britain' I. The splendour of birds of prey amongst the solitude of mountains was one of Wolf's favourite themes.*
(*Private Collection*)

Wolf soon attracted the interest of distinguished naturalists, and Gould, who already owned a small picture called 'Partridges Dusting', further commissioned from him an oil-painting 'Woodcocks Sheltering' which was shown at the Royal Academy in 1849. The woodcocks became firm favourites, and Wolf received many commissions, for he was particulary adept at depicting the subtle formations of feather tracts in various shadings of browns and showing the camouflage of game birds in their surroundings. When Wolf later illustrated the Woodcock for Gould's *Birds of Great Britain*, he was horrified by Richter's addition of wild hyacinths into the finished print. '*Much* too red' he said of the woodcock, 'and he must go and put in those blue-bells and things too! I can't be answerable for the colouring. Everything gets vulgarised'. In a letter to Mrs. Hugh Blackburn he said that Gould's birds showed detail without light, shade or perspective, and that the final prints were less like a bird than a 'mere map of its markings'.

The Zoological Society commissioned Wolf in 1852 to begin a series of 'Zoological Sketches' which were to be artistic records of the animals in their care. Wolf portrayed these life-like animals in the romantic settings of their distant homelands. He

Woodcock (Scolopax rusticola), lithograph by H.C. Richter from Wolf's drawing for 'Birds of Great Britain' IV. Wolf criticised Gould's plates for their over-bright hand-colouring, describing this woodcock as 'much too red', and disliking Richter's addition of 'bluebells'. (Oberton Trust)

could convey beautifully the atmosphere of landscape backgrounds, and in his illustrations for Gould's prints the ptarmigan crouches in the snow of the Scottish moors while the golden eagle glides by, the coot dabbles by the muddy river-bank, or the Icelandic Gyrfalcon perches on a crag in solitude.

Rock Ptarmigan (Lagopus mutus helveticus) *in winter plumage, a lithograph by Richter in 'Birds of Great Britain' IV from a drawing by Wolf. The adult birds squatting in the distance are camouflaged from the eyes of the golden eagle. (Osberton Trust)*

King Duck (Somateria spectabilis), *a watercolour study in reverse by Joseph Wolf, signed and dated 1857, for the lithograph credited to J. Gould and H.C. Richter in 'Birds of Great Britain' V. Gould greatly admired Wolf's work; this fault in acknowledgment was probably an oversight. (Private Collection)*

Blackcock (Tetrao tetrix), *a watercolour study by Joseph Wolf, for 'Birds of Great Britain' IV. In his notes Gould described the black grouse's eyebrow as 'covered with fine papilliae like a pile of velvet, beautiful blood scarlet'. (Private Collection)*

Rock Ptarmigan (Lagopus mutus helveticus) *in summer plumage, a watercolour study, signed and dated 1856, by Wolf for Richter's lithograph in 'Birds of Great Britain' IV. The setting is the Snee Hatten mountains, Norway, where Gould and Wolf observed the ptarmigan breeding. (Private collection)*

Coot (Fulica atra), *watercolour study by Wolf signed and dated 1857, for Richter's lithograph for 'Birds of Great Britain' IV. Gould wrote that the size of the coot's 'pearly milk white pointed knob . . . is near the breadth of a shilling as possible'. (Lambourne collection)*

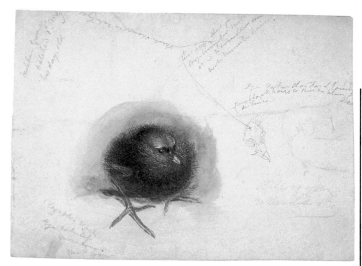

Moorhen chick (Gallinula chloropus) *a watercolour study by an unknown hand. Gould remarked on the 'peculiar colouring' of the chick in its first few days while feathers replace its down. (Spencer Library, University of Kansas).*

Moorhen (Gallinula chloropus), *an exact watercolour study signed by Joseph Wolf, for Richter's lithograph in 'Birds of Great Britain' IV. Gould proudly described the colouring of this newly-hatched brood as 'nearly as portraits . . . as Mr Wolf or Mr Richter could render them'. (Private Collection)*

Red-throated Bluebreast (Cyanecula suecica), *this drawing, in pencil and watercolour, signed J. Gould F.R.S., is an exact study for Richter's lithograph in 'Birds of Great Britain', II. Gould sketched and made notes from a bluebreast specimen shot in Norway in July 1856, where he and Wolf had watched the bird nesting. (Spencer Library, University of Kansas)*

In the summer of 1856 Gould and Wolf travelled to Norway, and at farmhouse lodgings at Hjerkin, in the mountains of the Dourefjeld district, Gould skinned the specimens that they shot and drew. Wolf claimed he was the better field naturalist, for amongst other successes he led the way to the hidden red-throated bluebreast's nest by recognising its song, a discovery which Gould said in his text was made by chance. Gould's notes on the bluebreast describe a Hjerkin skin which had a 'red spot on its breast which shows but little unless the neck be stretched'. The two ornithologists watched the buzzard, ptarmigan, golden plover, brambling and fieldfare breeding, but strangely the fieldfare's plate in the *Birds of Great Britain* was not by Wolf, but from Richter's drawing of a specimen shot near Maidenhead on 18th April 1864.

Palmer's biography reveals Wolf as a rugged individualist, and it is hardly surprising that this gifted artist did not become one of Gould's regular team. Although a fine lithographer, Wolf did not draw on stone for Gould, but contributed vigorous charcoal drawings and water-colour studies – A.H. Palmer implied that these were drawn casually on paper supplied by Gould, by way of friendship, while Gould paced about ready with a reward of a fourpenny cigar!

Inquisitive Neighbours (1875), a charcoal drawing by Joseph Wolf in which an indignant ring dove is loosening her wings to give some red squirrels 'a good buffet'. The drawing belonged to Wolf's biographer A.H. Palmer. It is a final study for a picture used in Palmer's 'Life of Joseph Wolf'; two earlier sketches exist, one in the Victoria and Albert Museum. (Lambourne Collection)

Shoebills (Balaeniceps rex), a watercolour by Joseph Wolf showing the gigantic storks in the romantic setting of their homeland, the Upper Nile. These were painted from the first live shoebills in the Zoological Gardens, 1869. Wolf had earlier illustrated Gould's description of a shoebill in Zoological Proceedings, 1851, from a skin. (Aves Folio 84, Vol. 5, Zoological Society, London)

Wolf and his Hobby (1890) by Lance Calkin. Originally the 70-year-old Joseph Wolf was depicted, characteristically, with a cigar in his hand. But Wolf substituted a hawk to commemorate his life-long devotion to birds of prey. (Zoological Society, London)

On other occasions, Palmer relates, Gould would arrive at Wolf's studio with a rare skin (sometimes borrowed) for the *Birds of Asia*, 'help himself to a cigar', and ask for an immediate sketch or water-colour to be made. In his text Gould expressed great admiration for Wolf's illustrations, particularly the birds of prey, but Wolf considered the majority of Gould's routine plates were prosaic or expressionless. He preferred to show dramatic situations in his work, and his illustrations for Gould show the osprey with its prey of fish, the gannet on a clifftop amongst a noisy nesting colony, or the snowy owl immobile against a background of prowling polar bears.

From the middle of the 1870's Gould's health was poor, and he suffered from a chronic and painful illness. But he still continued to work, and he never lost interest in birds. Dr. Bowdler Sharpe, who completed Gould's unfinished work after his death, talked of Gould in old age: 'It was always a real pleasure to see the delight which animated the old naturalist when, in his invalid days, I took some new form of bird such as Bulwer's Pheasant to be figured in the *Birds of Asia*. On the latter occasion he exclaimed there was only one man in the world who could do justice to such a splendid creature and that was Mr. Wolf; who, at his request, at once designed a beautiful picture which appeared in the *Birds of Asia*'.

Another account of Gould in old age occurs in

John Guille Millais's biography of his father, Sir John Everett Millais, President of the Royal Academy. John Guille Millais visited Gould at Charlotte Street with a friend who was a keen collector of bird-of-paradise skins, and wished to purchase some rare specimens.

Millais records his impression of Gould, then in his seventies: 'He was at that time a confirmed invalid and confined to his couch, and when a drawer full of birds was placed on his lap he would slowly and solemnly lift the lid and handle the specimens his fingers trembling with emotion'. With much persuasion and tact Millais's friend was able to buy some skins at a high price. Much to Millais's surprise, Gould, who was then averse to strangers, asked to see his father, Sir John Everett Millais, and an appointment was made, probably in the last year of Gould's life.

Gould sat propped up on his couch for the occasion and, calling his daughters to help him, showed his visitors 'his latest gems from New Guinea and the Papuan Islands, and afterwards his unique collection of humming-birds, all of which were set up in cases, and may be seen (alas! with diminished lustre) in the Natural History Museum at South Kensington'.

Sir John Millais was delighted with all he saw and

Bulwer's Pheasant (Lobiophasis bulweri), *lithograph by Richter from Joseph Wolf's drawing for 'Birds of Asia' VII. Gould, an invalid in old age, was always delighted when the young naturalist Richard Bowdler Sharpe showed him the latest rare pheasant skin. Wolf drew this at Gould's request from a specimen borrowed from the British Museum. (Osberton Trust)*

Formosan Jay (Garrulus taivanus), drawn in pencil and watercolour and attributed to Richter for his lithograph in the 'Birds of Asia' V. Some annotations are by Gould; 'trace spots on wing' was added by Richter. (Spencer Library, University of Kansas)

on his way home said 'That's a fine subject: a very fine subject. I shall paint it when I have time.' The resolution was carried out, for 'The Ruling Passion' was exhibited at the Royal Academy in 1885. It shows an elderly ornithologist lying on his couch, scrutinising a bird specimen, surrounded by stuffed creatures. But there the parallel with Gould's situation ended. As a model for the ornithologist Millais used an elderly engraver, who, with scull-cap and spectacles, looked completely different from Gould in old age. Two little boys in the painting were Millais's grandsons, 'Bubbles' and his brother George, the others mostly professional sitters, and the birds were from John Guille Millais's collection.

Unhappily, the crowded, cheerful family scene which Millais portrayed was not true to Gould's own life. Of Gould's six children his three sons were missing – two dead and one abroad. John Henry, the eldest, a doctor, had died in Bombay, when only 25; and Franklin, also a doctor, had died, aged 33, on board ship in the Red Sea, after a visit to India accompanying the Duke of Westminster's grandson, Lord Belgrave. Charles Gould was a geologist. He surveyed in Tasmania, wrote a scholarly book called *Mythical Monsters* in 1886, about legendary dragons and other creatures, and died in Montevideo in 1893. When Gould's eldest daughter, Eliza, married the widower John Musket, Gould said she 'was leaving one old man for another'! A daughter of their marriage, who was four years old at Gould's death, was the only grandchild.

After Gould died the new Natural History Museum was completed at South Kensington, with Sir Richard Owen, who had fought hard for the zoological collections to be moved from the British Museum at Bloomsbury, as Director. Gould's collection of 12,395 specimens, including over 5000 humming-birds was bought by the museum for £3000. This collection excluded the Australian specimens which had been bought by the Philadelphia Academy in 1847. From Gould's office there survived thirty tons of surplus book materials, texts, drawings, proofs, tracings and experimental prints, which were bought by Henry Sotheran, booksellers, and remained, almost unexamined in various basements and warehouses, wrapped in parcels until 1937. They were dispersed in sales, and much of the stock was bought by Ralph N. Ellis, who left it to the University of Kansas in 1945.

Two years after Gould's death Sir Richard Owen recalled the visits of his friend to his garden at Sheen Lodge, in Richmond Park. Owen was collecting for

'The Ruling Passion' (1885) by Sir John Everett Millais was painted after Gould's death, but was inspired by a visit to his house in the last year of his life. The figures were painted from Millais's own family and models, and the birds from his son John Guille Millais's collection. (Glasgow Art Gallery)

his 'garden book' the names of all the birds he could see. 'The list, however, would have been incomplete without the aid of my lamented friend, John Gould. It was ever with him a favourite summer afternoon's holiday, after a ramble in the park, to pass an hour in the garden. On one of these occasions, in early June, we rested on a seat by a weeping ash, but allowing a full view of the garden. Happening to show him my ornithological list at that date, Gould said 'You have got more birds in the garden than I see here, I expect'. Now he possessed in a remarkable degree the faculty of imitating the various notes of all our vocal species. He bade us sit still and be silent, then began. After emitting a particular 'motivo' for a few minutes, he would quietly point to a little bird which had flown from an adjoining bush upon the lawn, and was there hopping to and fro, gradually nearing the locality of the specific song. We could then recognise the species to which Gould gave the name. This attraction and its result was repeated, and we enjoyed the same instructive amusement on subsequent summer vacations, to which I am indebted for additions that would otherwise probably have escaped my observation'.

This tribute to John Gould, the 'Bird Man', is a fitting ending to the story of a remarkable life.

Bibliography

Dr. Gordon Sauer's book *John Gould: the Bird Man* contains a full bibliography of works on John Gould. The following list is a brief introduction.

Anker, J. *Bird Books and Bird Art*, Copenhagen 1938

Barber, L. *The Heyday of Natural History, 1820-70*, Cape, London 1980

Barclay-Smith, P. *Garden Birds*, King Penguin, London 1945

Bowdler Sharpe, R. *An analytical index to the works of the late John Gould*. Sotheran, London 1893

Blunt, W. *The Ark in the Park*, Hamish Hamilton, London 1976

Chisholm, A. H. *The Story of Mrs. Elizabeth Gould*, Melbourne 1944

Chisholm, A. H. *An Explorer and His Birds. John Gilbert's Discoveries in 1844-45*. Melbourne 1945

Chisholm, A. H. *Strange New World. The Adventures of John Gilbert and Ludwig Leichhardt*, Sydney 1955

Corning, H. *Letters of John James Audubon, 1826-40*, Boston 1930

Dance, P. *The Art of Natural History*, Country Life, London 1978

Darwin, C. *The Origin of the Species* First ed. 1859. Reprinted Dent, London 1971

Dixon, J. *Kangaroos, John Gould*, Macmillan, Australia 1973

Dixon, J. *Gould's Mammals* David and Charles, London 1977

Dyson, A. *Pictures to Print. The nineteenth century engraving trade*, Farrand Press 1984

Helyar, J. *History in the Making*, Kansas Alumni Magazine, January 1985

Hince, K. *Catalogue of Fine and Valuable Books dealing mainly with Natural History and Australian Discovery . . .* Melbourne 1985

Hullmandel, C. *The Art of Drawing on Stone*, Ackermann, London 1824 Facsimile, Garland, New York 1982

Jackson, C. E. *Bird Illustrators. Some artists in early lithography*. Witherby, London 1975

Jackson, C. E. H. *C. Richter – John Gould's unknown artist*. J. Soc. Biblphy nat. Hist. London 1978

Lysaght, A. M. *The Book of Birds*, Phaidon, London 1975

McEvey, A. *Collections of John Gould Manuscripts and Drawings*. La Trobe Library Journal, October 1968

McEvey, A. *John Gould's Contribution to British Art*. Sydney University Press, Australia 1973

McEvey, A. *John Gould's ability in drawing birds*. Art Bull of Victoria, Sydney University Press, Australia 1973

Mason, A. *John Gould: His Birds and Beasts*, Exhibit at the Kenneth Spencer Research Library, University of Kansas, 1981

Moorehead, A. *Darwin and the Beagle*, Penguin, London 1971

Noakes, V. *Edward Lear: the Life of a Wanderer*, Collins, London 1968

Noakes, V. *Edward Lear 1812-1888*, Royal Academy Exhibition, London 1985

Palmer, A. H. *The Life of Joseph Wolf*, Longmans, London 1895

Sauer, G. *John Gould, the Bird Man, A Chronology and Bibliography*, Lansdowne Editions, Melbourne, and Henry Sotheran, London 1982

Scherren, H. *The Zoological Society of London*, Cassell, London 1905

Sitwell, S. *Fine Bird Books, 1700-1900*, Collins, London 1953

Skipwith, P. *The great bird illustrators and their art, 1730-1930*, Hamlyn, London 1979

Twyman, M. *Lithography 1800-1850*, Oxford University Press, 1970

University of Kansas, *Books and Libraries at the University of Kansas*, 13:2 1976 for articles by C. Chittenden *On Birds and Bird Men*; A. McEvey, *John Gould – Some Unanswered Questions*; G. Sauer, *John Gould, artist? Testimony of the yellow-billed cuckoo.*

Index

Page numbers in bold type indicate an illustration.

A

ACKERMANN Rudolph 34
ADELAIDE, Australia 48,57
AITON John Townsend 21
ALBERT Prince 15,22,66,85
ALI Mehemet 23
AMSTERDAM 37
ANNING Mary 19
ANTWERP 97
ARACARI Chestnut-Eared 41
ARACARI Curl-crested 41
ARGYLL Duke of 95,96
ASIA S.S. 89
ASTOR LIBRARY, New York 66,94
AUDUBON John James 25,27 28,30,31,33,37,47,90
AUSTEN Jane 19

B

BACHMAN John 47,90
BAILY William 79,92
BAIRD Spencer Fullerton 94
BALFOUR AND NEWTON LIBRARY, Cambridge 50,56
BARBER Lynn 10,21
BARTRAM'S GARDENS, Philadelphia 79,92
BAT Gould's Wattled 16
BAYFIELD Mr. 76
BEAGLE S.S. 9,45,46
BERLIN 37
BERNE 37
BEWICK Thomas 14,30
BINNEY Dr. A 94
BIRD OF PARADISE 106
BIRD OF PARADISE Grey-Chested 87

BIRD OF PARADISE Papuan 86,87
BIRD OF PARADISE Red 86
BLACKBURN Mrs Hugh 95,96,98
BLACKCOCK 101
BLUEBREAST Red-Throated 68,102,103
BONAPARTE Prince Charles Lucian 9,90
BOSTON Mass. 92,94
BOWER-BIRD Spotted 50,51,52
BRITISH ASSOCIATION 37
BRITISH MUSEUM 14,47,73 109
BROAD STREET, Soho 14,52,75 85
BUCKLAND Frank 13
BUDGERIGAR 17,52

C

CABOT Dr 94
CHARLOTTE STREET 14,75 85,106
COCKATOO 33
COHN Walter, Walter & 10
COOK Captain 22
COOT 100,101
COXEN Charles 14,17,25
COXEN Elizabeth (later Gould) 25,26
COXEN Henry 56
COXEN Stephen 25
CUCKOO 95,96
CUCKOO Yellow-Billed 92

D

DANA Prof. James D. 94
DARWIN Charles 45,46,95,96
DERBY, Earl of 39
DIXON Joan 64
DOTTEREL 72
DOUGLAS David 90
DOVE Ring 103
DUCK King 101
DUCK Mallard 28,29

E

EAGLE Golden 100
EAGLE Sea 38,39
EDWARDS George 30
EGHAM Surrey 52
ELLIS Ralph N. 109
EMU 53
ETON 21
EUGENIE Empress of France 15
EWING Reverend 10
EYTON Thomas Campbell 45

F

FALCON White-Fronted 62
FIELDFARE 74,103
FINCH Gouldian 15,16
FINCH Large-Beaked 46
FOUNTAINE Margaret 13
FRANKLIN Capt. (Sir John) 25 31,48
FRANKLIN Lady 27,48,57

G

GALAPAGOS ISLANDS 46
GANNET 105
GEORGE IV 21,23
GILBERT John 16,47,50,56,57
GIRAFFE 23,24
GOULD Charles 89,92,93,94,107
GOULD Eliza 66,75,85,107
GOULD Elizabeth 9,15,26,27 34,36-38,40,46-52,56,57,59,64
GOULD Franklin Tasman 48 59,107
GOULD Henry (John Henry) 47 56,107
GRAY George Robert 47,55,97
GREAT EXHIBITION 1851 76,79
GREBE Little 69
GREBE Great-crested 8,10
GRISET Ernest 13
GROUSE Black 101
GUILLEMOT Common 70,71
GYRFALCON Greenland 97
GYRFALCON Icelandic 98,100

GYRFALCON White Greenland 96

H

HART William Matthew 9,42 66,73,75,86,87
HAVELL Robert 28
HAWKINS Benjamin Waterhouse 13,53,64
HERON Australian 49
HERRICK Edward C. 94
HOBART, Tasmania 48,55,56,57
HOBART ZOO 11
HOBBY 105
HULLMANDEL & WALTON 10 44
HULLMANDEL Charles 10,34 35,75,76
HUMMING-BIRDS 79,80,85,89 92,94,106,109
HUMMING-BIRD:
Bahama Wood-Star 83
Blue-breast 84
Blue-tailed Mango 82
Empress Brilliant 15
Green-headed Emerald 88
Green-headed Sapphire 81
Green-throated Inca 82
Phaon Comet 20
St. Domingo 81
Shining sun-beam 84
White-tailed Emerald 83

I

IGUANODON (model) 13
INGILBY Sir Thomas 22

J

JACKSON Christine 53
JARDINE Sir William 25,30,36 47,56
JAY Formosan 107

K

KANGAROO Great Red 65
KANGAROO S.S. 94

KANSAS, University of 109
KEW GARDENS 40
KIRTLAND Dr. Jared 94
KNOWSLEY menagerie 39,40

L

LAWRENCE George N. 92
LEAR Edward 9,25,**31**,33,34
36,37,40,44,50,64
LEICHARDT Ludwig 50
LEWIS G.H. 21
LEYDEN 37
LIBRARY OF PARLIAMENT,
Toronto, Canada 94
LILFORD Lord 78
LINNAEUS Carl 14
LINNEAN SOCIETY 15,23,76
LIZARS William 27
LORIKEET Swift **54**
LYME REGIS **18**,19

M

MACAW Blue & Yellow **32**,33
MACAW Red & Yellow 33
MALLARD 29
MAGPIE LARK **57**,61
MCKELLAR Captain 48
MILLAIS John Guille 106,107
MILLAIS Sir John Everett 106
107,**109**
MINTERN BROS 10
MOORHEN **102**
MUSKET John 107

N

NAPIER Lord 93
NATURAL HISTORY, Museum of,
London 14,67,86,106,109
NATURAL HISTORY,
Society of, Montreal 94
NATURAL SCIENCES,
Academy of, Philadelphia 14
67,92,94,109
NEWCASTLE UPON TYNE 30
NEW YORK CITY 89,90,92,94
NORWAY 101,103

O

OSBERTON 69 ,95
OWEN Sir Richard **12**,13,109
OWL Barn 38,**44**
OWL Eagle **37**
OWL Snowy 105

P

PALMER A.H. 97,103,105
PALMER Everard 94
PALMER Samuel 97
PARAKEET Warbling Grass 17
PARAKEET Yellow-Collared **60**
PARROT African Grey 22
PARSEE S.S. 47,48
PARTRIDGE Plumed 91
PENGUIN Crested 58
PETREL Short-Tailed 61
PHAON COMET 20
PHEASANT Bulwer's 105,**106**
PITTA Elegant **75** — **78**
PRINCE Edwin 9,47,66,67,89
PTARMIGAN 100,103
PTARMIGAN Rock **100,101**

Q

QUAIL **73**
QUEEN VICTORIA 15,52,66,85
QUETZAL **42**

R

RAMSGATE, Kent 25
REGENT'S PARK 23,25,79
RHEA Common 45
RHEA Darwin's 45
RICHTER Henry Constantine 9
40,53,55,64,66,73,75,86,98,103
RIPLEY CASTLE, Yorks 22
ROBIN **68,74**
ROME 44,50
ROOK **30**
ROTHSCHILD, Baron,
of Tring 13
ROTTERDAM 37

ROYAL ACADEMY 55,98
106,107
ROYAL SOCIETY 15
ROYAL SOCIETY OF
TASMANIA 48

S

SAND-MARTIN 69
SCHEGEL AND
WULVERHORST 97
SELBY Prideaux John 25,30,33,36
SENEFELDER Alois 34
SHARPE Dr. Richard Bowdler 34
78,86,105
SHEEN LODGE, Richmond 109
SHOEBILL **104**
SHRIKE **35**
SMITHSONIAN
INSTITUTION 94
SOTHERAN Henry 109
SQUIRREL Red **103**
STOKE HILL, Guildford 19
STUART R. L. 94
STURT Capt. 57
SULLOWAY Frank 46
SULPHUR H.M.S. 5,93
SWAINSON William 22,30,33,78
SWAN Bewick's **14**
SYDNEY, Australia 57,58

T

TASMANIA 27,48,56,57,59,107
TAYLOR & FRANCIS 9
TEMMICK Prof. Conrad 25,37
TERN Lesser 28
TERN Little 29
THOMPSON Flora 19
THRUSH Song **74**,75
TIGER Tasmanian 11
TIT Coal 68
TOOTH-BILL Equadorian 93
TOUCAN Black-Mandibled 41
TOUCAN Red-Billed 41
TOUCAN Toco 40
TROGON Elegant/Graceful 43

V

VAN DIEMAN'S LAND 16,**55**
VIGORS Nicholas 36

W

WALES, Princess of 85
WALKER Marion 5,21,73
WALLABY Yellow-Footed Rock **63**
WALTER WALTER & COHN 10
WALTON HALL, Yorks 11
WALTON Hullmandel & 10
WATER-RAIL **69**
WATERTON Charles 11,15,23
WHITE Reverend Gilbert 10
WILLIAM IV 24,36
WILSON Dr. T. B. 92
WINDSOR 21,23
WOLF Joseph 7,9,96,97,98
103,105
WOODCOCK 98,**99**
WOODPECKER Green **67**

Y

YARRUNDI, Australia 57,59

Z

ZOOLOGICAL GARDENS 69,73
79,85
ZOOLOGICAL SOCIETY,
London 23,24,25,26,33,36
37,44-47,66,79,90,98

112